The Story of Expecting You

The Pregnancy Journal
Memory Book
that Tells the Story
of Growing You

MEDICAL DISCLAIMER

The information contained in this book is not intended to and does not provide medical advice It is intended for informational purposes only and is not meant to be nor is it a substitute for professional medical advice, diagnosis, or treatment. Active and consistent prenatal care with a licensed medical professional throughout pregnancy facilitates early detection and treatment of potential concerns and reduces the risk of pregnancy and birth complications. Never ignore professional medical advice in seeking treatment because of any information contained in this book. If you think you may have a medical emergency, immediately call your doctor, or dial 911.

HEAR YOUR
STORY

TO MY INCREDIBLE CONTRIBUTORS

This book was written with the guidance, help, and consultation of many, including medical professionals, mothers, and a few moms-to-be. All my gratitude for their knowledge, insight, and collaboration

- Thank You, Thank You!

This book belongs to

_____

_____

My Due Date is

_____

FiRST
TRiMESTER

You have
my whole heart,
for
my whole life.

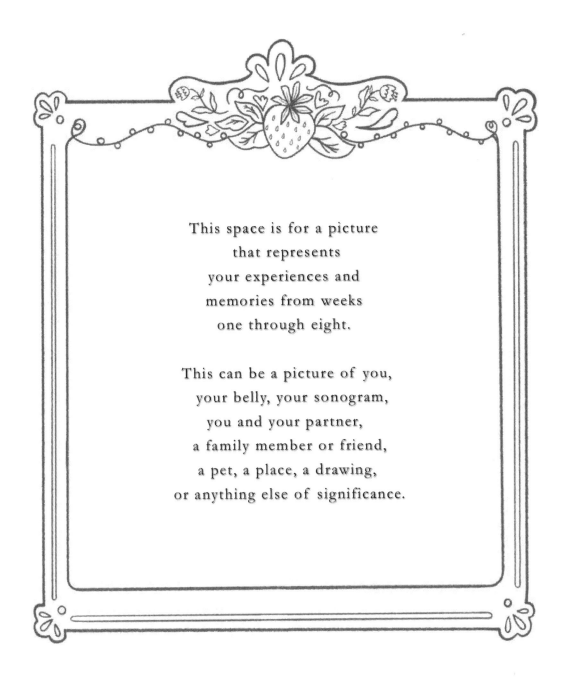

This space is for a picture
that represents
your experiences and
memories from weeks
one through eight.

This can be a picture of you,
your belly, your sonogram,
you and your partner,
a family member or friend,
a pet, a place, a drawing,
or anything else of significance.

Your First Eight Weeks

Weeks One to Four

"A grand adventure is about to begin."
— Winnie the Pooh

The first week of your forty-week "I'm having a baby" calendar is the first week of your last menstrual cycle. That means you most likely became pregnant in weeks three or four.

Your Due Date

"When are you due?"

"How far along are you?"

"Are you STILL pregnant?"

When you are pregnant, everyone will have questions and unsolicited opinions on the specifics of you and your pregnancy.

The conversation is often the same. It starts with a question about how far along you are. Your response is then quickly followed by their personal appraisal of how you look and how you must feel.

"You're so cute! You must be miserable in this heat!"

That will then lead to their lengthy list of things you should be doing and should not be doing.

In other words, the world is suddenly your doctor.

Just smile and say things like, "That's really helpful," or "You're so kind." Then laugh to yourself about the marvel and the mystery of having a baby.

You are on a unique journey, one where you will be relentlessly assessed and graded and evaluated by everyone. And by everyone, this means family, friends, and strangers alike. They will all have advice and opinions and will be quick to share them.

Consider this practice in perfecting your patience and flexibility, which is a good thing considering there will soon be a brand-new baby in your life.

Your Due Date

"Love yourself first, and everything else falls in line."
— Lucille Ball

The most important thing to know about your due date is that it is just an estimate.

Calculating the exact day your baby will be born requires knowing a long list of factors, with the most important being when you conceived.

Knowing this is a challenge because 1) ovulation can occur anytime from eleven to twenty-one days after your last period, 2) the sperm can fertilize the egg for up to a week, and 3) everyone is different.

This is a big part of why less than five percent of all births happen on the due date, and a "full-term" pregnancy can occur in weeks thirty-seven through forty-one.

Most doctors calculate the estimated due date by counting forward from the last period. With this method, day one of the pregnancy calendar is the first day of the last period and the due date is determined by counting forward forty weeks.

1. My last period started on this date...

_____

2. If I count forward from this date 280 days (forty weeks), I land on this date...

_____

This is the estimated date my baby will be born!

In later weeks, your doctor may adjust this date if ultrasound measurements suggest the birth will occur a week or more from the predicted due date.

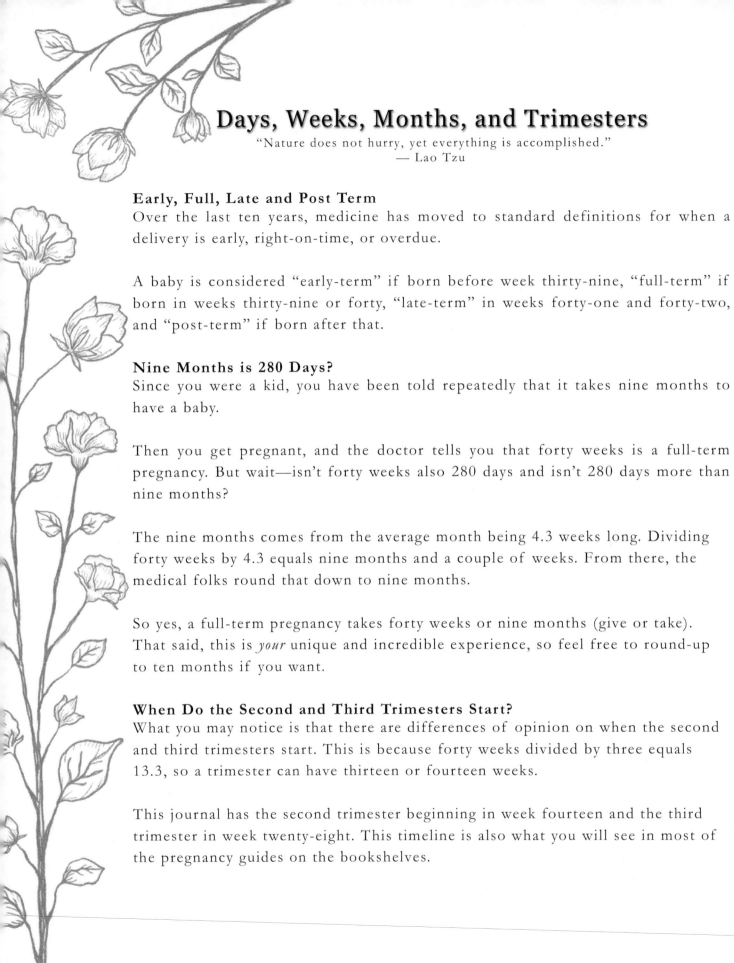

Days, Weeks, Months, and Trimesters

"Nature does not hurry, yet everything is accomplished."
— Lao Tzu

Early, Full, Late and Post Term

Over the last ten years, medicine has moved to standard definitions for when a delivery is early, right-on-time, or overdue.

A baby is considered "early-term" if born before week thirty-nine, "full-term" if born in weeks thirty-nine or forty, "late-term" in weeks forty-one and forty-two, and "post-term" if born after that.

Nine Months is 280 Days?

Since you were a kid, you have been told repeatedly that it takes nine months to have a baby.

Then you get pregnant, and the doctor tells you that forty weeks is a full-term pregnancy. But wait—isn't forty weeks also 280 days and isn't 280 days more than nine months?

The nine months comes from the average month being 4.3 weeks long. Dividing forty weeks by 4.3 equals nine months and a couple of weeks. From there, the medical folks round that down to nine months.

So yes, a full-term pregnancy takes forty weeks or nine months (give or take). That said, this is *your* unique and incredible experience, so feel free to round-up to ten months if you want.

When Do the Second and Third Trimesters Start?

What you may notice is that there are differences of opinion on when the second and third trimesters start. This is because forty weeks divided by three equals 13.3, so a trimester can have thirteen or fourteen weeks.

This journal has the second trimester beginning in week fourteen and the third trimester in week twenty-eight. This timeline is also what you will see in most of the pregnancy guides on the bookshelves.

Using This Book

"I guess I do believe in love at first sight."
— Author Unknown

The Story of Expecting You was designed to give you a place to tell your one-of-a-kind pregnancy story.

This is your special place to remember and record, to celebrate and care. Each week of the forty-week pregnancy calendar is explored and celebrated through thoughtful guided journal prompts, advice and support for key activities, and positive encouragement as you live these incredible moments.

Each week of this book also has a reminder to pause and dedicate time and attention to taking care of you. This journey will ask a lot of you and your body, and it's important to make taking care of you as much a priority as taking care of your baby.

This book has been crafted to inspire you and give you space to record your experiences. The pages within are dedicated to your exciting firsts, your intimate thoughts, and your moments to remember.

This is a place for your emotions and experiences, your celebrations, and challenges. Allow yourself to reflect and write with openness and you will create a legacy and gift for you and your growing little one.

There has never ever been anyone like you, a baby like yours, or the pregnancy story you two will share. These are the moments and memories of a lifetime, and this is your amazing story to tell.

Week Five

"Now my belly is as noble as my heart."
— Gabriela Mistral

Today's Date:

_____

The three words that best describe how I am feeling this week are:

1. _____

2. _____

3. _____

My energy level this week has been...

_____

_____

_____

I have been taking care of myself by...

_____

_____

_____

_____

_____

Your baby is 1/17ᵗʰ of an inch, about the size of a seed on a strawberry.

Week Five

"A child's first teacher is its mother."
— Peng Liyuan

When I think about my being pregnant, I get excited about...

_____

_____

_____

_____

_____

_____

_____

_____

_____

_____

This is the week the majority of expecting moms discover they are pregnant.

Week Five

"Motherhood: all love begins and ends there."
— Robert Browning

...and nervous about...

_____

_____

_____

_____

_____

If I find myself becoming uneasy, I will do the following to help myself calm these feelings...

_____

_____

_____

_____

_____

_____

Your body is beginning to produce larger levels of progesterone, which can drain your energy and cause some fatigue.

A Moment for You

"Beauty is how you feel inside."
— Sophia Loren

Over the next thirty-five weeks, you are going to be asked to do some incredible things. In addition to growing a baby, experiencing all it requires of you and your body, you may also find yourself with a long list of things to do before delivery day.

If all of this feels extremely overwhelming or makes you anxious, don't worry, you're not alone. The trick is to find a way to focus on the basics.

What are the basics?

The first and possibly most important thing is to get your rest. There is a long list of benefits for you and your baby if you are getting the needed amount of sleep.

Next basic: eliminate activities and habits that are potential risks to you and your baby's health.

Give your body the fuel it needs by eating a healthy diet and drinking lots of water. Also ensure your body gets the movement it needs with some doctor-approved daily exercise.

The last of the basics is to make yourself a priority by scheduling daily time for you to pause everything and focus on *your* needs. Try for a minimum of thirty minutes each day. Use this time to give yourself a chance to reset. Be in the moment and try to fully experience this daily pause.

Be patient with yourself and others. Don't hesitate to reach out to the people in your life when you need support. And most of all, never forget how incredible you are.

And now, three cheers for new experiences, and here's to creating and living the stories of your life!

Your little one's circulatory system is up and running with a heart that beats at twice the speed of yours.

Week Six

"Honey is sweet. A little baby is even sweeter."
— Author Unknown

Today's Date:

_____

The three words that best describe how I am feeling this week are:

1. _____

2. _____

3. _____

My energy level this week has been...

_____

_____

_____

I have been taking care of myself by...

_____

_____

_____

_____

Your baby is now a quarter of an inch long, about the size of an amethyst in a ring.

A Letter to...

"Babies are such a nice way to start people."
— Don Herold

A letter to myself as I begin my pregnancy journey...

_____

_____

_____

_____

_____

_____

_____

_____

Tiny buds that will become your baby's arms and legs have formed.

A Letter to...

"My soul saw you and said, 'Oh, there you are. I've been looking for you.'"
— Author Unknown

A letter to my baby as we begin Us...

_____

_____

_____

_____

_____

_____

_____

_____

_____

_____

_____

_____

Make sure to get enough Vitamin D as it plays a key role in the development of your baby's heart, kidneys, bones, and nervous system.

A Moment for You

"To fall in love with yourself is the first secret to happiness."
— Robert Morley

Sometime in the next few weeks, you are going to have this incredible moment...

You will be going about your day, minding your own business, doing your usual list of to-dos, when out of the blue, a bolt of awareness will strike, and you will suddenly grasp what you already know:

You Are

Having a

Baby!

That moment will be instantly followed by a billion overlapping emotions. You will feel yourself swinging from excited to concerned to jubilant to stunned to amazed to...

Don't worry about your back-and-forth feelings. Expecting a baby, especially a perfect baby like yours, is a lot to take in.

If you start to feel a little overwhelmed, remind yourself how incredible you are by making a list of the things you have already accomplished and achieved in life.

If you find yourself stuck or anxious, think of the positive things you have created in your life, including close relationships. Reach out to friends, family, or your doctor if you need someone to talk with.

This is going to be a magical experience and you are more than ready for it!

*At six weeks, your uterus is expanding, growing
from the size of a plum to about the size of an apple.*

Week Seven

*"There are two lasting bequests we can give our children.
One is roots. The other is wings."* — Hodding Carter Jr.

Today's Date:

_____

The three words that best describe how I am feeling this week are:

1. _____

2. _____

3. _____

My energy level this week has been...

_____

_____

_____

I have been taking care of myself by...

_____

_____

_____

_____

_____

Your baby is now a half inch long, the same size as a blueberry.

I'm Pregnant?

*"Being pregnant means every day is another day closer
to meeting the other love of my life." — Author Unknown*

The day I discovered I was pregnant was...

_____

I thought I might be pregnant because...

_____

_____

_____

The way I found out was...

_____

_____

_____

The sentence that best describes my reaction to the news is...

_____

_____

_____

_____

The first trimester is when your baby's organs and primary structures form.

I Mean, I'm Pregnant!

"A new baby is like the beginning of all things –
wonder, hope, a dream of possibilities." — Eda LeShan

The first person I told was...

_____

_____

This is the way I shared the news with them...

_____

_____

_____

_____

The thing I most remember about their reaction is...

_____

_____

_____

_____

Your baby's eyes now have their pupils, corneas, and lenses.

A Moment for You

*"Keep good company, read good books, love good things and
cultivate soul and body as faithfully as you can." — Louisa May Alcott*

We've all become accustomed to prioritizing other responsibilities over our personal needs.

Our days are built around to-do lists and work assignments. Evenings are spent emailing and texting, and bedtime includes looking through our phones while thinking about all the things we didn't do that day and will need to add to tomorrow's list of things that need to be completed.

None of this suddenly changes when you become pregnant. There is no pause on the lists and schedules, and it is easy to fall into the trap of spending your pregnancy trying to do everything at once, while also somehow, someway growing a healthy baby.

This is why it is important to set aside time that is just for you. Things often don't happen unless we schedule them, so now is the time to sit down with your planner and set aside time every day over the next two weeks (weeks seven and eight) that is just for you. This can be for any length of time but try for a minimum of thirty minutes each day.

Adding self-care to our day helps us manage the impacts of the toils and stresses of life.

- **Physical Self-Care** gives your body the rest, movement, and nutrition it needs. This can include exercise, eating the right foods, getting enough sleep, and keeping up your regular healthcare visits.
- **Mental Self-Care** develops and inspires your mind through activities such as reading, crafts, or learning something new.
- **Emotional Self-Care** helps you express and manage emotions.
- **Social Self-Care** is taking care of your relationships.
- **Spiritual Self-Care** provides you with a deeper sense of your place in the universe. Examples include prayer, meditation, journaling, and gratitude.

If it seems impossible to find time in your day, do a quick scan of what you are already doing and look for things or aspects of things that you can do differently, hand off to someone else, or simply not do.

Taking care of you is taking care of your baby.

Week Eight

"Happiness is Home Made."
— Author Unknown

Today's Date:

_____

The three words that best describe how I am feeling this week are:

1. _____

2. _____

3. _____

My energy level this week has been...

_____

_____

_____

I have been taking care of myself by...

_____

_____

_____

_____

Your baby is now about .04 ounces and .63 inches long, the size of a pearl.

Week Eight

"All that I am, or hope to be, I owe to my angel mother."
— Abraham Lincoln

All About Me as a Baby...

I was born on this day...

_____

In this city...

_____

And in this place...

_____

I was this long, and I weighed this much...

_____

My full name on the day I was born was...

_____

My parents were these ages when I was born...

_____

My first words were...

_____

_____

_____

I took my first steps when I was this old...

_____

Your little one has their taste buds (and yes, they are already grumbling about broccoli.)

Week Eight

"It takes fearlessness to be a mom, strength to raise a child, and love to care for someone more than you do for yourself." — Author Unknown

My favorite story of the day I was born is...

_____

_____

_____

_____

_____

_____

_____

_____

_____

_____

_____

Keep up with dental appointments, as pregnancy creates a higher risk for dental issues.

A Moment for You

"Always remember you are braver than you believe, stronger than you seem, and smarter than you think." — Christopher Robin

This is the time when the side effects of being pregnant can become more potent. For many women, the main thing they are having to deal with during this time is the discomfort of morning sickness.

If you are experiencing queasiness, try to keep track of it and avoid the foods, tastes, textures, or smells that are triggering. You may also find some relief in one or more of the following common methods for coping:

- Eat smaller, more frequent meals.
- Focus on foods that are high in protein and low in fat.
- Avoid spicy foods.
- When feeling bad, try limiting your diet to bland foods that are easy to digest. Examples include chicken, white rice, plain crackers, toast, pretzels, applesauce, bananas, watermelon, popsicles, and gelatin.
- Keep yourself hydrated.
- Try chewing ice.
- Ginger can help. You can find it in teas, candies, lozenges, or in drinks. Just make sure it is real (not artificial) ginger.
- Drink peppermint tea.
- Hard peppermint candies also help many.
- As does hard sour candies.
- Acupressure.
- Acupuncture.
- Take your prenatal vitamins with a snack or at bedtime.
- Hypnosis.
- Many women report that the smell of rosemary or fresh lemon help.
- Taking 25 milligrams of Vitamin B6 three times a day has been reported to provide some relief.
- Take a break or a day off.
- Let your co-worker or partner know if their lunch or perfume/cologne is triggering your nausea.
- Do not hesitate to see your doctor if things become intolerable.

Your baby's nose, lips, and ears are beginning to form.

Babies

are

bundles

of hope.

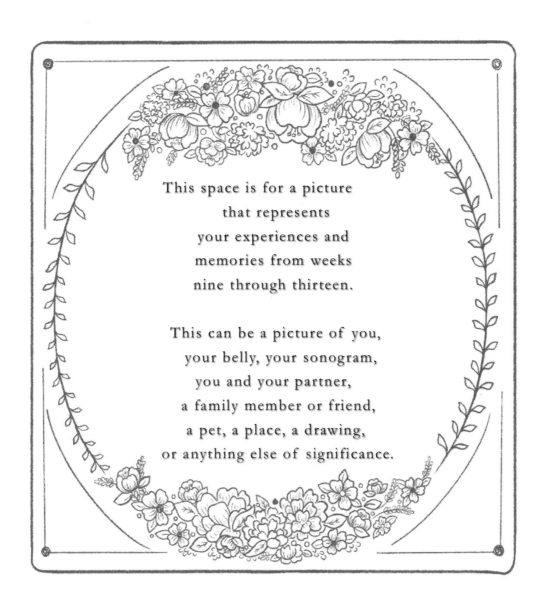

This space is for a picture
that represents
your experiences and
memories from weeks
nine through thirteen.

This can be a picture of you,
your belly, your sonogram,
you and your partner,
a family member or friend,
a pet, a place, a drawing,
or anything else of significance.

Weeks 9 to 13

Week Nine

"You are my definition of perfection."
— Author Unknown

Today's Date:

_____

The three words that best describe how I am feeling this week are:

1. _____

2. _____

3. _____

My energy level this week has been...

_____

_____

_____

I have been taking care of myself by...

_____

_____

_____

_____

Your baby is 0.9 inches long, slightly bigger than the diameter of a nickel.

Week Nine

"No matter how much I say I love you, I always love you more than that."
— Author Unknown

When I was a kid, I imagined life as an adult would be like...

Avoid your cat's litter as it can harbor a toxoplasmosis infection-causing parasite.

Week Nine

"A happy family is but an earlier heaven."
— George Bernard Shaw

When I compare my life now to what I imagined it would be like, I applaud and congratulate myself for accomplishing the following...

_____

_____

_____

_____

_____

When I compare my life to what I imagined it would be, I find myself inspired to achieve these goals...

_____

_____

_____

_____

_____

The tiny buds that are your baby's hands and feet are developing tiny fingers and toes.

A Moment for You

"To fall in love with yourself is the first secret to happiness."
— Robert Morley

In week seven, you scheduled yourself some daily self-care time.

Looking back over the last two weeks, ask yourself how that went. Were you able to take time every day? If not, what was the reason? Were there times of the day when it was easier to take this time than others?

When you were able to take it, what were the activities that helped you the most to relax and reset?

Using your experiences from weeks seven and eight, schedule daily self-care time for the next four weeks (weeks nine through twelve). As before, try for a minimum of thirty minutes each day. This is especially great to do on busy days because those are the ones where you will need this time the most.

Looking back over the last two weeks, the activities that helped me relax, rest, and take care of myself the most were...

_____

_____

_____

_____

_____

_____

The eyelids have formed and will stay sealed over the eyes until week twenty-eight.

Week Ten

"A benefit of pregnancy is you can blame your swearing and bad temper on hormones."
— Author Unknown

Today's Date:

_____

The three words that best describe how I am feeling this week are:

1. _____

2. _____

3. _____

My energy level this week has been...

_____

_____

_____

I have been taking care of myself by...

_____

_____

_____

_____

_____

Your baby is about 1.2 inches long, the diameter of a half dollar coin.

Week Ten

"Like stars are to the sky, so are the children to our world."
— Chinonye J. Chidolue

The things I miss the most from my pre-pregnancy life are...

_____

_____

_____

_____

Of all the things I have experienced during the first ten weeks of my pregnancy, the one that has surprised me the most is...

_____

_____

_____

_____

_____

Ten weeks means you only have three more weeks until the end of the first trimester.

Week Ten

"A perfect example of minority rule is a baby in the house."
— Author Unknown

The hardest thing I have had to deal with so far during my pregnancy is...

_____

_____

_____

_____

_____

Going through this experience has reminded me and taught me the following about myself...

_____

_____

_____

_____

_____

At ten weeks, your baby is officially in the fetal stage of development.

A Moment for You

"Part of taking care of your baby is taking care of yourself."
— Author Unknown

Maintaining an optimistic outlook on life can help reduce stress, increase happiness and motivation, and make us better at managing normal life challenges.

One of the best ways to increase our optimism is to spend time each day focusing on the positive things in our lives. Practice this by writing down your ten favorite things about having a baby.

1. _____

2. _____

3. _____

4. _____

5. _____

6. _____

7. _____

8. _____

9. _____

10. _____

Avoid hot baths and hot tubs. The rise in your internal body temperature can harm your developing baby.

Picking a Name

"It Ain't what they call you, it's what you answer to."
— W.C. Fields

There are a million different ways that soon-to-be parents pick their baby's name.

In some cases, the selection occurred long before the mother even became pregnant. In others, the decision wasn't final until after the baby was delivered.

Whatever your process, here are a few things you may want to keep in mind when making your selection:

1. Picking a very popular name may mean they will "share" it with a bunch of their peers. Remember in third grade when there were four Christopher's and six Brittany's?

2. You should similarly consider the opposite: rare names are often rare for a really good reason.

3. Picking a name is a wonderful way to honor you and your child's cultural background.

4. It is also a good idea to be careful when considering names that are unique to a cultural background different from your child's.

5. Avoid trends. No one wants their child's name to be hip for a day and then, later, a reminder of an awkward long ago pop culture phase that few remember.

6. When considering a name inspired by someone famous, recognize that today's much-loved person may be tomorrow's sad tale.

7. Picking a name that has a strong positive or negative association with someone or something else can cloud the world's first impressions and interactions with your child throughout their life.

8. Review the initials of the name you select. Christopher Owen Wilson is COW and Pamela Isabella Gibson is PIG.

9. Remember that people often shorten names. William Michael Judge may end up being known as Will Judge.

10. Creative spellings and pronunciations for common names will result in your child and you spending the rest of your days correcting teachers, bosses, and everyone else.

In 2020, the most popular female gender names were Luna, Maeve, Aurora, Olivia, and Isla.

Picking a Name

"The beginning of wisdom is to call things by their right names."
— Confucius

11. Remember the time when the entire world shook their head and said out loud, "That poor child!" when the actor/musician/other person named their kid after an animal or fruit or inanimate object? Just a reminder.

12. In this online world of ours, it is a good idea to pick a name that can be easily found in a search engine. Crystal Hunter gets you people who search for gems, and Austin Cook gets you want ads for restaurants in Texas.

13. Don't let the opinions of others (and there will be many) sway you from a name you love.

14. Then again, if every person you tell crinkles up their nose and makes a face when they hear the name...might be something to consider.

15. Say out loud names you are contemplating many, many times. How does it sound? Is it easy to say? Do the words work together? Is the rhythm pleasant to the ear? Is the sound too close for comfort to other words you don't want other kids using when saying your child's name?

16. Try to avoid feeling pressured or anxious when selecting the name. Go with what YOU like and remember that you don't have to make the final decision until you complete the paperwork for the birth certificate.

17. Picking a name that is similar in sound or spelling to a sibling's name can cause confusion.

18. Picking a name that both parents are excited about is always a great goal.

19. Alexa. Yes, it is a name. It is even a very pleasant name. But...

In 2020, the most popular male gender names were Milo, Asher, Atticus, Oliver, and Levi.

Name Worksheet

"A good name is rather to be chosen than riches."
— King Solomon

Names we are considering...

_____

_____

_____

_____

_____

_____

_____

_____

_____

_____

_____

In 2020, the most popular gender-neutral
names were Ellis, Phoenix, Remy, Marlowe, and Shea.

Name Worksheet

Names we are considering...

_____

_____

_____

_____

_____

_____

_____

_____

_____

_____

_____

Federal records show that there are over 1,000 people with identical first and last names. Think "Rose Rose" or "Thomas Thomas."

Week Eleven

*"Being a mother is not about what you gave up to have a child,
but what you gained from having one." — Author Unknown*

Today's Date:

_____

The three words that best describe how I am feeling this week are:

1. _____

2. _____

3. _____

My energy level this week has been...

_____

_____

_____

I have been taking care of myself by...

_____

_____

_____

_____

At 1.6 inches long, your baby is about the size of a Brussels sprout.

Week Eleven

"I loved you from the start. You stole my breath, embraced my heart.
Our life together has just begun. You are part of me." — Author Unknown

Lately, the main things I have been craving are...

_____

_____

_____

_____

My most memorable dream from the past few months is...

_____

_____

_____

_____

_____

_____

_____

_____

Your baby weighs nearly a quarter of an ounce, the same as three pennies.

Week Eleven

"A mother's love for her child is the most supreme of all loves."
— Author Unknown

Week eleven means two more weeks left in my first trimester. Right now, I am noticing the following changes in my body, feelings, and emotions:

_____

_____

_____

_____

_____

_____

_____

_____

_____

_____

*To help you understand your options and rights, make sure you study
your company's maternity leave policies and state's family leave laws.*

A Moment for You

"Adopt the pace of nature: her secret is patience."
— Ralph Waldo Emerson

The end of the first trimester (week 13) is often when many expecting parents begin to share their news with a larger circle of family and friends. There are also many who wait until later in their pregnancy.

The important thing to remember is that this is your pregnancy and your baby, and you get to decide when and how and with whom you share the news.

Spend some time daydreaming about how you want to announce that you are expecting. Imagine how specific people will react. Who will be the most surprised? Who will say, "I knew it!"? Who will cry?

When I am ready, I am thinking about announcing my pregnancy by...

_____

_____

_____

_____

_____

_____

_____

*If you are using antacids to calm your heartburn
and indigestion, avoid brands that contain magnesium.*

Week Twelve

"God could not be everywhere, and therefore he made mothers."
— Rudyard Kipling

Today's Date:

_____

The three words that best describe how I am feeling this week are:

1. _____

2. _____

3. _____

My energy level this week has been...

_____

_____

_____

I have been taking care of myself by...

_____

_____

_____

_____

Your baby is now a little over two inches long, similar in size to a lime.

Week Twelve

"Of all the rights of women, the greatest is to be a mother."
— Lin Yutang

The sentence that best describes my reaction and feelings the first time I heard my baby's heartbeat is...

_____

_____

_____

The person I most wish was here to experience this journey with me is...

_____

_____

_____

Being pregnant has made me sentimental for...

_____

_____

_____

They are now quickly growing, doubling in size over the last three weeks...

Week Twelve

"A baby makes love stronger, the days shorter, the nights
longer, savings smaller, and a home happier." — Author Unknown

As I approach the end of my first trimester, the biggest help I could use to get everything done every day is ....

_____

_____

_____

_____

A few ideas on how I can make my life easier or get assistance elsewhere are...

_____

_____

_____

_____

Your baby's digestive system is up and running. This includes
their stomach, esophagus, intestines, pancreas, liver, and kidneys

A Moment for You

*"How we judge ourselves has more impact on who we are
and what we do than the total of the judgments of others." — Author Unknown*

Whether you are a first-time or experienced mom-to-be, it's fun to keep track of all the "firsts" you and your baby get to experience.

Firsts

My first ultrasound was on...

_____

The first time I had a pregnancy food craving, it was for...

_____

The first time I wore maternity clothing was in week...

_____

The first baby gift I received was given to me by...

_____

The gift they gave us was...

_____

_____

The first item of baby clothes I bought was...

_____

The first thing I bought for the baby's nursery was...

_____

The first time I became emotional about a baby-related thing was...

_____

*By this point, the placenta has taken over producing
the hormones needed to get through the rest of your pregnancy*

Baby Budget

*"A parent is someone who carries pictures where
their money used to be." — Author Unknown*

While the nurse won't scan your baby at a register as you leave the delivery room,
you should be aware that these little people come with a hefty price tag.

Various studies show that the average cost to deliver a baby is $1,750, and the price
tag to raise a baby from the day of birth to the day they turn eighteen years of age
can get up to $250,000.

And that doesn't include college and braces and tutors and sports and birthdays
and school pictures and proms and...

It is astonishing how the addition of one small person to the family can impact
your household finances so heavily. It won't be long until things that you barely
knew existed a month ago are filling your shopping cart and reducing your bank
account.

One key is to start planning now.

A good first step is to determine your current monthly spending, total debt, and
how much you are saving of each paycheck.

Now do the math on what the first year of having a baby will cost. Common
expenses include childcare, diapers, and formula (if not breast feeding). Divide that
number by twelve.

Add this number to your current monthly spending and this will give you an idea of
the impact on your budget.

Now look for ways to reduce your spending. Common ways include cooking more
meals at home, fewer splurges, less online shopping, and avoiding impulse
purchases.

*Your baby's tiny heart is beating around 170 beats a minute.
To compare, the typical adult resting heart rate is between 60 and 100.*

Baby Budget

"The person who doesn't know where his next dollar is coming from often doesn't know where his last dollar went." — Author Unknown

Other ways to reduce your spending include:

- Make and stick to a budget.
- Shop around to get a better monthly rate on your cell phone, internet, and cable services.
- Do you really need to subscribe to all those streaming services?
- Speaking of subscriptions, look through your bank and credit card statements for recurring monthly charges that you don't need.
- Search for cheaper home and auto insurance.
- Grocery shop with (and stick to) a shopping list.
- Limit your trips to the grocery store.
- Reduce your use of food delivery services.
- Get a better gym rate (or drop it if you never go or can work out at home).
- Use discounts and coupons.
- Buy second-hand.
- Limit your credit card use.
- Reducing your debt will lower your monthly outgoing expenses.
- Unsubscribe from company mailing lists to avoid receiving emails that. tempt you to spend with sales and special offers.
- Avoid spontaneous purchases by setting a rule that says you have to wait 48 to 72 hours before buying anything over a specific dollar amount.
- Seek out free or cheap entertainment options. Ideas include movies at home, picnics, walks, and getting together with friends or family.

Lowering your monthly spending now will help you get used to living on less than what you're used to, help you to pay off any debt faster than planned, and help you to save for tomorrow.

Disposable diapers can cost .11 to .38 cents per diaper, an amount that can add up to around $600 to $700 a year (or more).

Baby Budget

"A goal without a plan is just a wish."
— Antoine de Saint-Exupéry

One-time expenses:

(These are great items to add to your baby registry.)

- ☐ Breast pump (insurance will often pay for one)
- ☐ Crib, crib mattress, sheets, and blankets
- ☐ Dresser
- ☐ Changing table (you can also use the dresser top)
- ☐ Playpen
- ☐ Highchair
- ☐ Stroller
- ☐ Safety gates
- ☐ Baby monitor
- ☐ Baby bathtub (the sink also works great)
- ☐ Baby thermometer
- ☐ Baby nail clippers
- ☐ Bibs
- ☐ Clothes
- ☐ Bassinet
- ☐ First-aid kit
- ☐ Baby carrier
- ☐ Car seat (avoid using a used car seat)
- ☐ Diaper bag
- ☐ Nursery decorations, paint, etc.
- ☐ Rocking chair
- ☐ Booster seat
- ☐ Co-pays for delivery day

Polls of new parents consistently show that the cost of childcare is their highest monthly household expense.

Baby Budget

"I make myself rich by making my wants few."
— Henry David Thoreau

Recurring monthly expenses:

- ☐ Baby bottles
- ☐ Childcare
- ☐ Babysitters
- ☐ Diapers or diaper service
- ☐ Wipes
- ☐ Formula (if not breast feeding)
- ☐ Bottles
- ☐ Sippy cups
- ☐ Baby food once they start eating solids
- ☐ Laundry expenses (babies go through a lot of clothes!)
- ☐ Toiletries (baby shampoo, body wash)
- ☐ Teething rings and ointment
- ☐ Books
- ☐ Toys
- ☐ Health insurance
- ☐ Life insurance
- ☐ Savings for emergencies/unexpected costs
- ☐ Savings for college
- ☐ Co-pays for medical visits
- ☐ More baby clothes as they quickly outgrow everything
- ☐ Assorted items such as pacifiers, swaddles, and baby booties

A good resource for finding the average cost of childcare in your state is www.epi.org/child-care-costs-in-the-united-states.

Week Thirteen

"There is only one perfect child in the world, and every mother has it."
— Author Unknown

Today's Date:

_____

The three words that best describe how I am feeling this week are:

1. _____

2. _____

3. _____

My energy level this week has been...

_____

_____

_____

I have been taking care of myself by...

_____

_____

_____

_____

Your baby is a little less than three inches long, about the same size as a peapod.

Week Thirteen

"You never understand life until it grows inside of you."
— Sandra C. Kassis

Week thirteen means I am at the end of the first trimester of my pregnancy. Looking back over this time, I am very proud of myself for...

_____

_____

_____

_____

_____

_____

_____

_____

_____

Fine hair called lanugo has begun to appear and will soon cover your baby.

Week Thirteen

"I have my dreams of you to guide, help, and
hold me through the long wait." — Mary Soukop

The song that best describes my first trimester is...

_____

_____

_____

A few of my most favorite memories from the first trimester are...

_____

_____

_____

_____

_____

_____

_____

_____

Your baby is now producing urine, adding to the surrounding amniotic fluid.

A Moment for You

"Don't sacrifice yourself too much, because if you sacrifice too much there's nothing else you can give." — Karl Lagerfeld

Take a few minutes to schedule your daily self-care time for the next four weeks (weeks thirteen through sixteen). As before, try for a minimum of thirty minutes each day and add in an hour or more at least once a week.

It is week thirteen and you and your baby have officially arrived at the end of the first trimester of pregnancy.

This is the perfect time to pause and remind yourself of all you and your baby have accomplished over the past three months (hint: there is a lot.)

Here is a list of a few of the highlights:

- You became pregnant!
- You started a few good habits and got rid of unhelpful or risky habits.
- You grew your baby from a fertilized egg to an embryo and then to the fetal stage.
- Your little one has developed their vital organs, a heartbeat, facial features, arms, legs, fingerprints, and a brain.
- You experienced and persevered through a (too long) list of pregnancy-related "side effects."
- You are seeing yourself in a whole new way.
- You are being reminded of how magical life can be.

In other words,

You Are

Doing

Miracle Stuff!

At week thirteen, the risk of having a miscarriage drops to 1%.

Notes

Notes

SECOND
TRIMESTER

Hold them a little longer,
rock a little more.

Read another story,
you've already read them four.

Let them sleep on your shoulder,
rejoice in a happy smile.

They are only little
for such a little while.

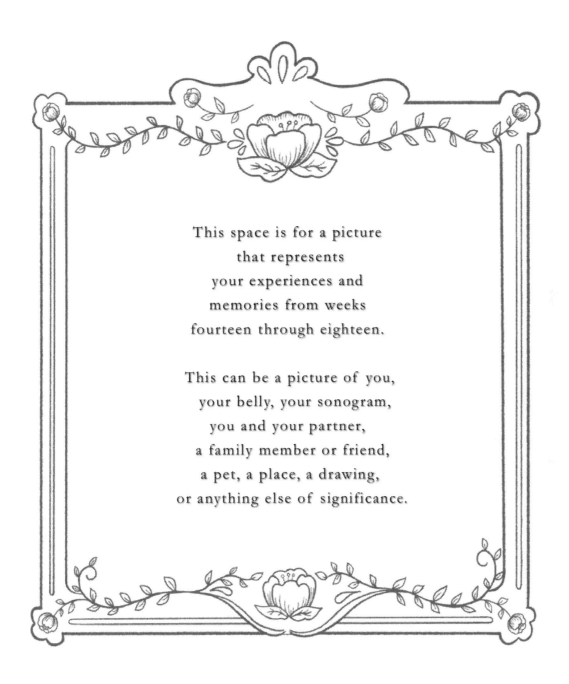

This space is for a picture
that represents
your experiences and
memories from weeks
fourteen through eighteen.

This can be a picture of you,
your belly, your sonogram,
you and your partner,
a family member or friend,
a pet, a place, a drawing,
or anything else of significance.

Weeks 14 to 18

Week Fourteen

"Life is always a rich and steady time when you are waiting for something to happen or to hatch." — E.B. White

Today's Date:

_____

The three words that best describe how I am feeling this week are:

1. _____

2. _____

3. _____

My energy level this week has been...

_____

_____

_____

I have been taking care of myself by...

_____

_____

_____

_____

Your baby has grown to be about three and half inches long, the size of a lemon.

Week Fourteen

"What good mothers and fathers instinctively feel like doing for their babies is usually best after all." — Benjamin Spock

A letter to myself as I start my second trimester...

_____

_____

_____

_____

_____

_____

_____

_____

_____

_____

Your baby can now make facial expressions!

Week Fourteen

"A baby fills a place in your heart that you never knew was empty."
— Author Unknown

A letter to my growing baby as we get closer to their birthday...

_____

_____

_____

_____

_____

_____

_____

_____

_____

_____

_____

Have you scheduled your childbirth classes?

A Moment for You

"Perfection only exists in babies and pastries."
— Gayle Wray

For many, the second trimester is the most pleasant period of their pregnancy.

You are showing, but not at the point where you are uncomfortable and it's an exertion to move around. Best of all, the morning sickness is lessening if not gone altogether, and your energy and appetite are increasing.

This is a great time to work on that "My Baby is Coming" to-do list. Getting started now will help you avoid having a long list of things to do in your last few months of your pregnancy.

Continue to designate time in your day for you. If you are looking for new ways to relax and reset, consider a few of the following:

- Start that book/audiobook everyone has been talking about.
- Re-visit a favorite television series.
- Start a new hobby.
- Get a subscription to a gossip magazine.
- Take an online class.
- Watch a documentary or docuseries on a topic you want to learn more about.
- Take an in-person or online yoga class.

This is also the time when many expecting moms start adding maternity clothes to their daily wardrobe. Treat yourself to a day of shopping for a few pregnancy-tailored items of clothing.

Emphasize day-to-day wear but also pick up one or two items for formal moments, for when you're feeling a little fancy. At a minimum, it is a good idea to invest in a few pairs of maternity jeans, leggings, t-shirts, and maternity bras and underwear.

Over the next four weeks, your baby will grow to be just under seven ounces.

Maternity Clothes Shopping List

"You know you're getting old when your friends start having kids on purpose."
— Author Unknown

The Basics:

- ☐ **Underwear.** Give yourself something pretty and comfortable.

- ☐ **Support bras.** You may want to go ahead and buy nursing bras instead of maternity bras to get the extra support you need and to save money later. Keep in mind that most women add a cup size when they begin breast feeding.

- ☐ **Leggings.** Always a good go-to.

- ☐ **Maternity jeans.** Many find full-panel maternity jeans more comfortable than the denim panel style.

- ☐ **A belly band** will allow you to wear that favorite pair of jeans well into your pregnancy.

- ☐ **Maternity dresses** are perfect for the warmer months and can be paired with a cardigan or denim jacket in the fall.

- ☐ **Twinsets** can fit any occasion and make it easy to cool down or warm up.

- ☐ **A few stretchy, simple dresses.** Get at least one in black for dressier moments. You can often find great options in non-maternity wear.

- ☐ **Comfy pajamas.** For those cozy nights in.

- ☐ **Soft and comfortable t-shirts** are one of the most versatile items you can buy for yourself.

- ☐ **Cute stretchy maxiskirts.** Why not?

- ☐ **Tunic tops** are practical, fashionable, and can be worn before and after you deliver.

- ☐ **Maternity shorts** if you will be pregnant in the summer months.

- ☐ **Oversized blazer.** Perfect for dressing up jeans or leggings.

Remember to reserve a doula if you will be using one.

Maternity Clothes Shopping List

"A mom's hug lasts long after she lets go."
— Author Unknown

My maternity clothes shopping list:

Your little one now has vocal cords!

Week Fifteen

*"Babies smile in their sleep because they're listening
to the whispering of angels."* — Author Unknown

Today's Date:

_____

The three words that best describe how I am feeling this week are:

1. _____

2. _____

3. _____

My energy level this week has been...

_____

_____

_____

I have been taking care of myself by...

_____

_____

_____

_____

_____

*Your baby is looking more like, well, a baby. Their facial features
are recognizable, and the head, body, arms, and legs are more proportional.*

A Moment for You

"The most important relationship is the one you have with yourself." — Diane Von Furstenberg

Week fifteen means you are in month four of your pregnancy and just a few weeks away from the halfway point.

This is a good week to start the exciting process of creating your baby's nursery. The fun of exploring the countless possibilities is also a great way to detach and distract yourself from the stress of daily responsibilities.

You can find fun ideas from online sites like Pinterest, Etsy, and Houzz.com.

While exploring all the possibilities can be exciting, making the final decisions can feel daunting. If you find yourself stuck and unable to decide, try a few of the following:

- Start with an overall theme for the room. Ideas can be a favorite children's book, a memorable vacation, or something from nature. You can also use a cherished item as inspiration for the whole room (for example, a hand-me-down stuffed animal could inspire a jungle, zoo, or baby animals theme.)
- Unsure about colors? Professional decorators will usually limit themselves to three colors and use the 60-30-10 rule.
  - 60% of the room's color palette comes from the walls (paint or wallpaper), the floor (carpets or rugs), and a larger piece of furniture.
  - The secondary color would add 30% of the overall palette and could be used for things like drapes, a smaller piece of furniture, and bed linens.
  - The accent color makes up 10% of the palette and could come from items such as artwork, lamps, and throw pillows.

If you will be working after your baby is born, this is a good time to start researching your childcare options. Many day-care centers have long waitlists.

Nursery Planning

"A toddler can do more in one unsupervised moment than most people can do all day." — Author Unknown

When I close my eyes, this is how I picture my baby's nursery:

_____

_____

_____

_____

_____

_____

_____

_____

_____

_____

Your baby now measures about four inches long, the size of an apple.

Nursery Planning

"If evolution really works, how come mothers only have two hands?"
— Milton Berle

A few helpful tips on planning your nursery:

- When looking at pictures of nurseries, write down what you like and don't like about the layout and decorations. Look for common themes and ideas in your "likes."

- Give the room a major scrubbing down before you start.

- Remember to place the crib away from windows.

- Ensure the furniture is sturdy and that the dresser, shelves, and changing table are securely bolted to a wall. You can get easy-to-use kits for this at your local hardware store or online.

- Repurposed or used furniture will have your friends asking where you found that beautiful one-of-a-kind piece.

- Consider using furniture that wouldn't be out of place when you upgrade the room from baby to child.

- Make sure you give yourself a comfortable chair in the nursery for those nighttime feedings.

- Firmly secure all wall hangings.

- Babies have more stuff than you can imagine, so plan now for designated areas and places for storage.

- Avoid long drapes and keep the blinds' pull strings up high.

- Black out curtains will help your little one sleep during the daytime.

- Think about installing a dimming switch so you can control how much light you shine into the room during those nighttime feedings.

- Baby proof the nursery now. You will be amazed how quickly your little one is crawling and walking and moving about on their own.

At fifteen weeks, your baby can move their entire tiny (but growing) body.

Plan Your Baby's Room

"Let them sleep, for when they wake, they will move mountains."
— Author Unknown

Nursery Shopping

"While we try to teach our children all about life, our
children teach us what life is all about." — Author Unknown

My nursery shopping list:

_____

_____

_____

_____

_____

_____

_____

_____

_____

_____

Nosebleeds are common with pregnancy but see your doctor if they become constant.

Week Sixteen

"Every newborn baby is the sun rising to a beautiful new day."
— Author Unknown

Today's Date:

_____

The three words that best describe how I am feeling this week are:

1. _____

2. _____

3. _____

My energy level this week has been...

_____

_____

_____

I have been taking care of myself by...

_____

_____

_____

_____

Your baby is a little over four and a half inches long, the size of an avocado.

Week Sixteen

"It's tempting to make pregnancy nine months of cheat days."
— Author Unknown

I began sharing the news of my pregnancy with a wider circle of people on this date:

_____

The most memorable reaction was...

_____

_____

_____

_____

_____

The most surprising reaction was...

_____

_____

_____

_____

_____

Week sixteen is the end of the fourth month of the pregnancy calendar.

Week Sixteen

"Expecting a baby is the beginning of some of life's most precious moments."
— Author Unknown

The three most interesting things people said when they heard the news were...

1. _____

_____

2. _____

_____

3. _____

_____

The five people I know I will be able to lean on for support, comfort, and advice during my pregnancy and after delivery are...

1. _____

2. _____

3. _____

4. _____

5. _____

Your little one's heart is beating between 150 to 180 times per minute.

A Moment for You

"The care, therefore, of every man's soul belongs unto himself."
— John Locke

The mid-pregnancy ultrasound usually occurs in weeks seventeen to twenty-one. This scan will check on how well your baby is growing, look for any issues, and confirm the delivery date.

Another thing the ultrasound might be able to identify is the birth gender. Because of this, make sure to tell the technician and your doctor if you don't want to know what it is (surprises can be fun.)

Another fun thing to do at this stage is play with a few of the many ways folklore and legends claim your baby's gender is revealed. These include:

- Moms with excessive morning sickness have girls.
- Carrying your baby high means a girl and low signifies a boy.
- If your bump sticks straight out, it's a girl. If it is wide, a boy.
- Babies with a heartrate over 140 are girls.
- Hot and sweaty during pregnancy? You're having a girl.
- A glowing, flawless complexion means a boy.
- French folklore claims that a pregnant mom that gains very little weight in her legs will have a girl.
- If you crave sweets, it's a boy; salty or sour means a girl.
- Craving citrus? You're having a girl.
- Brittle fingernails and hair mean it's a girl and nonstop dry hands, a boy.
- Acne outbreaks during your pregnancy? Girl.
- If you dream about your baby, legend says the gender will be the opposite of what you dreamt.
- The ring test is done by tying a favorite ring to a length of string and holding it over your pregnant belly. Circular swings mean a boy; back and forth, a girl.
- The Chinese gender chart compares your age when you conceived with the month of conception to predict the birth gender. There are dozens available online.

Your baby will grow about twelve inches in length from weeks thirteen to twenty-seven.

Week Seventeen

"Each and every baby is a new flower in the garden of our world."
— Author Unknown

Today's Date:

_____

The three words that best describe how I am feeling this week are:

1. _____

2. _____

3. _____

My energy level this week has been...

_____

_____

_____

I have been taking care of myself by...

_____

_____

_____

_____

_____

Your baby is about the size of a pear, fitting snugly in the palm of your hand.

Week Seventeen

"Every child begins the world again."
— Henry David Thoreau

The traits I admire most in my mother are...

_____

_____

_____

_____

_____

The traits I admire most in my father are...

_____

_____

_____

_____

_____

Your little one is getting stronger as their muscles continue to develop.

Week Seventeen

"Babies are bits of star-dust blown from the hand of God."
— Larry Barretto

My personal characteristics and traits that I think will help me to be a good parent are...

_____

_____

_____

_____

And these are the traits and parts of my personality that, as I become a new parent, I may need to increase awareness of, minimize and/or change...

_____

_____

_____

_____

_____

_____

Your baby's body is filling out and becoming more proportional with their head.

A Moment for You

"Love makes the belly go round."
— Author Unknown

Sit down and schedule daily self-care time over the next four weeks (weeks seventeen through twenty). Try for a minimum of thirty minutes each day, and make sure to also set aside an hour or more just for you at least every week.

Some of the best advice my parents ever gave me was...

This is a good week to start a list of what you want on your baby registry.

Week Eighteen

"One of life's greatest miracles is to have life grow from you."
— Author Unknown

Today's Date:

_____

The three words that best describe how I am feeling this week are:

1. _____

2. _____

3. _____

My energy level this week has been...

_____

_____

_____

I have been taking care of myself by...

_____

_____

_____

_____

_____

Your baby's tiny fingers now have tiny fingerprints.

Week Eighteen

"Sometimes the smallest things take up the most room in your heart."
— A.A. Milne

I would describe myself when I was a kid this way...

_____

_____

_____

_____

_____

The toy or item I most fondly remember from my childhood is...

_____

_____

_____

A family tradition I am excited to have my new baby be a part of is...

_____

_____

_____

_____

Lying on your left side can help your sleep be more restful.

Week Eighteen

"Moms are the glue that holds everything together,
even when they feel they are falling apart." — Author Unknown

A memory from my childhood that always makes me smile is...

_____

_____

_____

_____

_____

_____

_____

_____

_____

_____

_____

At eighteen weeks, your baby is almost six inches long and weighs
six and a half ounces, about the size of a large heirloom tomato.

A Moment for You

"Know thyself, for once we know ourselves,
we may learn how to care for ourselves." — Socrates

While it is natural to compare your pregnancy with others and things you read and hear, remember that each pregnancy is as unique and special as the baby that is born.

A few things to consider are:
- First pregnancies differ from seconds and thirds and on and on.
- The age of the mom-to-be can be a factor.
- Body type and fitness level can have an impact.
- Pre-existing medical conditions are often a sizeable factor.

Before you become concerned that your experience isn't matching what all the "advice" is telling you, remember that this pregnancy is this pregnancy and everybody and every *body* are different.

Follow your doctor's guidance but make sure the care you are being provided is tailored to you and your baby's specific needs. Learn from what others went through, but don't judge yourself because your experience is different.

This pregnancy belongs to you and your baby. Experience it for what it is. Delight in its uniqueness and celebrate its one-and-only magic and individual story.

There will never be another like this one.

I have many wonderful unique qualities. One that I am especially proud of is...

_____

_____

_____

_____

Your growing belly may decrease your overall balance. This may make everyday movements suddenly a challenge. Be extra careful!

No one

prepared me

for how much

I would

love you...

This space is for a picture
that represents
your experiences and
memories from weeks
nineteen through twenty-three.

This can be a picture of you,
your belly, your sonogram,
you and your partner,
a family member or friend,
a pet, a place, a drawing,
or anything else of significance.

Weeks 19 to 23

Week Nineteen

"Babies are always more trouble than you thought — and more wonderful."
— Charles Osgood

Today's Date:

_____

The three words that best describe how I am feeling this week are:

1. _____

2. _____

3. _____

My energy level this week has been...

_____

_____

_____

I have been taking care of myself by...

_____

_____

_____

_____

Your baby is a little over six inches long, about the length of a dollar bill.

Week Nineteen

"A mother's arms are made of tenderness and children sleep soundly in them."
— Victor Hugo

When I dream my biggest dreams for my baby, I wish for them a life that looks like...

Using a stretch mark cream can help your skin keep its resilience.

Week Nineteen

"Words cannot express the joy of new life."
— Hermann Hesse

When I dream my biggest dreams for myself, I wish for a life that looks like...

_____

_____

_____

_____

_____

_____

_____

_____

_____

_____

_____

A neti pot is a great non-medicine way to soothe a stuffy nose.

A Moment for You

"Mind. Body. Soul. These are the three things self-care is all about."
— Kathy Sledge

It's week nineteen and you may be feeling the impact of the higher levels of the hormone relaxin being produced by your body.

The good news is that this increase in relaxin will help make delivery day easier by loosening the pelvic ligaments, enlarging the cervix, and relaxing the uterine muscles. The downside is it can also cause back and joint aches and make your balance unsteady.

If you are dealing with these aches and pains, try a few of the following:
- Avoid shoes with poor arch support.
- Use a footrest when sitting for extended periods of time.
- During the day, regularly alternate between sitting and standing.
- Take an occasional walk.
- Stretch or do yoga.
- Take a warm (not hot) bath.
- Use heat compresses.
- Sleep on your side.
- Sleep with a pregnancy pillow.
- Regular doctor-approved exercise can also help your core and back muscles stay limber and strong.
- Talk to your doctor before taking any over the counter, homeopathic, or prescribed medication to relieve pain.

Pregnancy aches and pains are also a great excuse for getting a prenatal massage.

This is a massage that has been adapted to allow you to comfortably lie face down by using cushions and/or table openings. If you want a big day of pampering (after all, you *do* deserve it), many spas offer special pregnancy packages that include a massage, facial, manicure, and pedicure.

Your baby is moving more, but don't worry if you're not feeling anything. Many, especially with first pregnancies, won't feel anything until later weeks.

Week Twenty

"Mother is a verb. It's something you do. Not just who you are."
— Dorothy Canfield Fisher

Today's Date:

_____

The three words that best describe how I am feeling this week are:

1. _____

2. _____

3. _____

My energy level this week has been...

_____

_____

_____

I have been taking care of myself by...

_____

_____

_____

_____

In week twenty, your baby is sleeping twelve to fourteen hours a day (don't be jealous.)

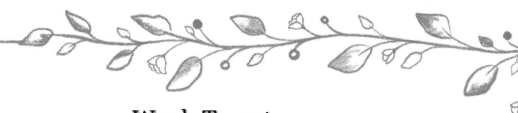

Week Twenty

"It is a moment of pure ecstasy and satisfaction when you see a smile flicker on a baby's lips, just as they gently pass into a deep slumber." — Author Unknown

As I approach the halfway point of my pregnancy, I am proud of myself and my baby for accomplishing the following...

_____

_____

_____

_____

_____

_____

_____

_____

_____

_____

Your baby's heartbeat is strong enough to be heard with a stethoscope.

Week Twenty

"You're my favorite reason to lose sleep."
— Author Unknown

The top ten things I love about being pregnant are...

1. _____

2. _____

3. _____

4. _____

5. _____

6. _____

7. _____

8. _____

9. _____

10. _____

This is a good time to contact your doctor and schedule your glucose test.

A Moment for You

You are probably becoming more and more visibly pregnant (not that one should ever ask a stranger if they are pregnant). This is a great excuse to treat yourself to some of those cute maternity clothes to show off your growing belly.

By the way, week twenty means you are halfway to delivery day! Sounds like a good reason to pause and celebrate all you have accomplished.

Delivery day

is right around

the corner!

Now is a good time to look through and prioritize the list of things you would like to have done before delivery day. Focus on the key items and don't be bashful about asking for a little help.

But most importantly, don't create any stress for yourself.

Date Night

While it may be hard to imagine it right now, you aren't that far away from the time when you will have delivered and be taking care of a newborn.

You will also likely find that you will have less flexibility to do many of the activities you currently take for granted. Things like dinner out, seeing a movie or play, or an evening out with friends.

If you are feeling up to it, make a reservation at a restaurant you love. Maybe include a movie or an evening of music or a play.

Your baby is now about nine inches long, about the size of a large artichoke.

Week Twenty-One

"How can something so small capture so much of my world?"
— Author Unknown

Today's Date:

_____

The three words that best describe how I am feeling this week are:

1. _____

2. _____

3. _____

My energy level this week has been...

_____

_____

_____

I have been taking care of myself by...

_____

_____

_____

_____

Your baby is ten and a half inches long, the same width as a standard dinner plate.

Week Twenty-One

"Children have more need of models than critics."
— French Saying

The name we selected for our new baby is...

_____

This is when we decided that this was the name...

_____

We picked this name because...

_____

_____

_____

_____

_____

When I say my baby's name out loud, it makes me think of...

_____

_____

_____

Carrying a few healthy snacks during the day can help calm pangs of hunger.

Week Twenty-One

"Every child born into the world is a new thought of God, an ever-fresh and radiant possibility." — Gilbert Parker

Growing up, my family would sometimes call me by this nickname...

_____

_____

_____

I got this nickname because...

_____

_____

_____

_____

_____

I sometimes call my growing baby the following nicknames:

_____

_____

_____

Avoid sleeping on your back. Your growing little one is now heavy enough to press against your intestines, organs, and larger blood vessels.

A Moment for You

"Not including ourselves in our compassion leaves out the most critical piece of our ability to truly help others." — Author Unknown

Okay, time to take out your planner and set aside daily YOU time for the next four weeks (weeks twenty-one through twenty-four). Try for a minimum of thirty minutes each day and an extra hour at least once a week.

Did I Really Just Feel That?
The first time you feel your baby move can be both startling and exciting. Each kick and turn and twist spurs your imagination and you can't help but wonder and guess what they will be like and who they will become.

The date that I felt my baby move for the first time was...

_____

Feeling them move for the first time caused me to react this way...

_____

_____

_____

_____

And feel this way...

_____

_____

_____

Over the past four weeks, your baby almost doubled in length.

Week Twenty-Two

"Tomorrow is the reward for being safe today."
— Author Unknown

Today's Date:

_____

The three words that best describe how I am feeling this week are:

1. _____

2. _____

3. _____

My energy level this week has been...

_____

_____

_____

I have been taking care of myself by...

_____

_____

_____

_____

*Your baby is a little under eleven inches in length,
or about the same length as a strand of uncooked spaghetti.*

Week Twenty-Two

"Carrying a baby is the most rewarding experience a woman can enjoy."
— Jayne Mansfield

For me, the qualities of a good friendship are...

_____

_____

_____

_____

Based upon the above, my closest friendships are with these individuals:

_____

_____

_____

_____

Ranking myself on a scale of one to ten (one is lowest and ten is awesome), I would give myself the following score for how I have been the last few months with balancing my needs, friendships, family, work, and my pregnancy.

_____

At this point, babies can hear sounds from the outside world so start practicing those lullabies and chatting it up with your little one.

Week Twenty-Two

*"Birth takes a woman's deepest fears about herself and
shows her that she is stronger than them." — Author Unknown*

Being pregnant can sometimes take us away from time with friends and family. I am
taking care of my relationships by doing the following...

_____

_____

_____

_____

_____

_____

_____

_____

_____

_____

_____

At week twenty-two, your baby weighs about one pound, the same as a can of soup.

A Moment for You

"The greatest gift you can ever give your child is to make sure you are taking care of you." — J.C. Samuelson

Weeks twenty-one through twenty-eight are an ideal time for a "babymoon" or getaway trip. This is the window when you may have less morning sickness, more energy, and your "bump" isn't getting in the way yet.

Run your plans by your doctor and try to avoid long flights and car rides. Also, do the just-in-case thing and get the address of a medical facility at your destination that's covered by your insurance.

Most importantly, rest, relax, and have fun.

Before my baby is born, I would like to visit these people and places:

_____

_____

_____

_____

_____

_____

_____

Your baby's tiny eyes are starting to develop their tear ducts.

Week Twenty-Three

*"Before you were conceived, I wanted you. Before you were born, I loved you.
Before you were here an hour, I would die for you."* — Maureen Hawkins

Today's Date:

_____

The three words that best describe how I am feeling this week are:

1. _____

2. _____

3. _____

My energy level this week has been...

_____

_____

_____

I have been taking care of myself by...

_____

_____

_____

_____

Week twenty-three means you are in your sixth month of pregnancy.

Week Twenty-Three

"A mother's joy begins when new life is stirring inside, a tiny heartbeat is heard for the first time, and a playful kick reminds her that she is never alone." — Author Unknown

If I wrote a book about this pregnancy, the title would be...

_____

_____

_____

_____

Being pregnant has made me more appreciative of these things...

_____

_____

_____

_____

_____

_____

_____

_____

_____

At eleven and a half inches long, your baby is about the size of a large mango.

Week Twenty-Three

"The art of mothering is to teach the art of living to children."
— Elaine Heffner

The song that always brightens my mood is...

_____

_____

The last time I was truly calm, relaxed, and at peace was...

_____

_____

_____

Three simple things that I can do every day to help myself feel rested, balanced, and happy are...

1. _____

_____

2. _____

_____

3. _____

In week twenty-three, your little one now weighs more than a pound.

A Moment for You

"How can I be so absent-minded when I have two brains in my body?"
— Pamela Lynn

Your doctor will probably schedule your glucose challenge test sometime in weeks twenty-four through twenty-eight.

This test helps your doctor understand your risk for gestational diabetes. On average, two to five percent of pregnant women are diagnosed with this condition, with a higher occurrence in those over the age of thirty-five, overweight, or with a family history of diabetes.

Common treatments can include a change in diet, scheduled exercise, daily monitoring of your glucose, and insulin.

If you are found to have gestational diabetes, it is critical that you closely follow your doctor's advice to reduce the risks for you and your baby. Doing so will also help quickly resolve the condition post-delivery.

Staying Active

Staying active during your pregnancy is a key part of maintaining you and your growing baby's health. A perfect way to do this is to set aside time each day for a thirty-minute walk.

Walking is a low-impact, low-stress way to add movement and exercise to your day. It can increase your energy, relieve stress, and has been shown to reduce the chances of gestational diabetes, pre-term delivery, and an unplanned cesarean delivery.

When walking, wear comfortable shoes, bring water, and avoid going on excessively hot or cold days. Be sure to listen to your body if you are feeling dizzy, overworked, or fatigued.

Most importantly, verify with your doctor before starting anything strenuous.

With seventeen weeks until your due date, it is a good idea to finalize your childcare options if you will be working after your baby is born.

Having you
has made so
much of life
make sense.

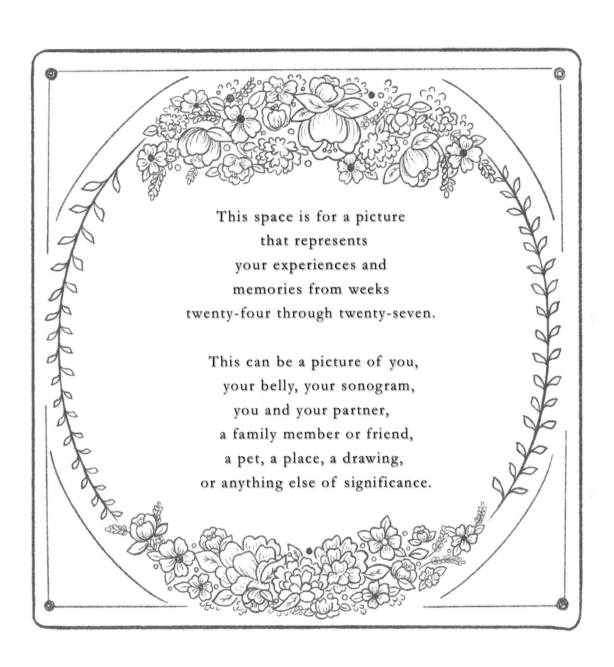

This space is for a picture
that represents
your experiences and
memories from weeks
twenty-four through twenty-seven.

This can be a picture of you,
your belly, your sonogram,
you and your partner,
a family member or friend,
a pet, a place, a drawing,
or anything else of significance.

Weeks 24 to 27

Week Twenty-Four

*"I think, at a child's birth, if a mother could ask a fairy godmother to endow
it with the most useful gift, that gift would be curiosity." — Eleanor Roosevelt*

Today's Date:

_____

The three words that best describe how I am feeling this week are:

1. _____

2. _____

3. _____

My energy level this week has been...

_____

_____

_____

I have been taking care of myself by...

_____

_____

_____

_____

_____

Your little one is about twelve inches long, the same length as an ear of corn.

Week Twenty-Four

"Each time I see my pregnant self in the mirror, I am reminded of all I can do and all I can be." — Author Unknown

When I was a kid, I remember loving these books...

_____

_____

_____

_____

_____

The books I look forward to reading to my baby are...

_____

_____

_____

_____

_____

Remember to keep hydrated. You and your baby are putting in some heavy work.

Week Twenty-Four

"When your wife is pregnant, don't eat the last ANYTHING."
— Author Unknown

A few of the things I am excited to teach my child are...

_____

_____

_____

_____

_____

A few of the experiences I can't wait to share with them are...

_____

_____

_____

_____

_____

Eyebrows and eyelashes are in place and hair is growing on the top of their head.

A Moment for You

"To love oneself is the beginning of a lifelong romance."
— Oscar Wilde

The second trimester is: a growing belly, multiplying pregnancy hormones, a moving baby, and aches and pains.

All these aspects can make sleeping a chore, if not sometimes impossible.

Equally frustrating can be how, once you finally get to sleep, you end up spending the night shifting and turning, trying to get comfortable.

A few tips to help you sleep better:
- Consider avoiding caffeine.
- Lower the temperature in your room at night. A chilly environment can help you relax and rest.
- Avoid going to bed with a full stomach.
- Watch your fluid intake around bedtime.
- Sleep on your side with a pillow along your back and a second between your knees.

While it doesn't typically fit how we think about marriage and partnership, don't hesitate to consider sleeping alone if it will help you maximize your rest.

Pregnancy Pillows
Treat yourself to a pregnancy pillow.

Pregnancy pillows provide extra support for you as your body changes to accommodate your growing baby. They come in a variety of shapes, sizes, materials, and fillings to hug and comfort your pregnant body as you sleep.

Pregnancy pillows prevent sleeping on your stomach or back, relieve back and hip pressure, and keep your body in better alignment. This promotes a more restful sleep, less back pain, leg cramps, heartburn, and nighttime congestion.

Week twenty-four means you are at the six-month mark (give or take).

Week Twenty-Five

"Give yourself the same care and attention that you give
to others and watch yourself bloom." — Author Unknown

Today's Date:

_____

The three words that best describe how I am feeling this week are:

1. _____

2. _____

3. _____

My energy level this week has been...

_____

_____

_____

I have been taking care of myself by...

_____

_____

_____

_____

In week twenty-five your baby weighs about the same as a head of lettuce.

Week Twenty-Five

"There are no words that can describe the euphoria you feel when your baby recognizes you for the first time and smiles." — Jared Padalecki

The last time I did something that was just for me was...

_____

_____

_____

_____

_____

The last time I remember being over-the-moon happy was...

_____

_____

_____

_____

_____

Your baby has grown almost two inches in the last seven days.

Week Twenty-Five

"Life doesn't come with a manual; it comes with a mother."
— Author Unknown

I am proud of myself for this completely-unrelated-to-being-pregnant reason...

_____

_____

_____

_____

_____

A few of the many things I love about myself include...

_____

_____

_____

_____

_____

_____

Your baby's sense of smell is now working.

A Moment for You

"An empty lantern provides no light."
— Author Unknown

Take a few moments to schedule your daily self-care time over the next four weeks (weeks twenty-five through twenty-eight). Try for the daily thirty minutes minimum and the extra added hour every week.

Hey, Are You Pregnant?

This is the time when your baby bump is becoming more and more noticeable. Your baby is adding about half a pound each week and your body is doing the necessary expansion to make room.

This is also a time when heartburn, swollen feet, leg cramps, body aches, hot flashes, and dizziness can become more common.

If you are dealing with swollen feet, you may get some relief by wearing comfortable loose-fitting clothes and avoiding uncomfortable shoes. Put your feet up when you can and avoid long periods of standing to help reduce the pooling of fluids.

Make sure you are drinking enough water, try to keep the caffeine to a minimum, and watch your sodium intake. Epsom salt baths are a great treat for tired feet.

More Firsts

The first time I was asked if I was pregnant was...

_____

_____

The first time someone asked if they could touch my belly was...

_____

_____

My reaction when they asked was...

_____

_____

_____

_____

_____

At this point you may notice a pattern in your baby's movements, where they are active and calm at similar times each day.

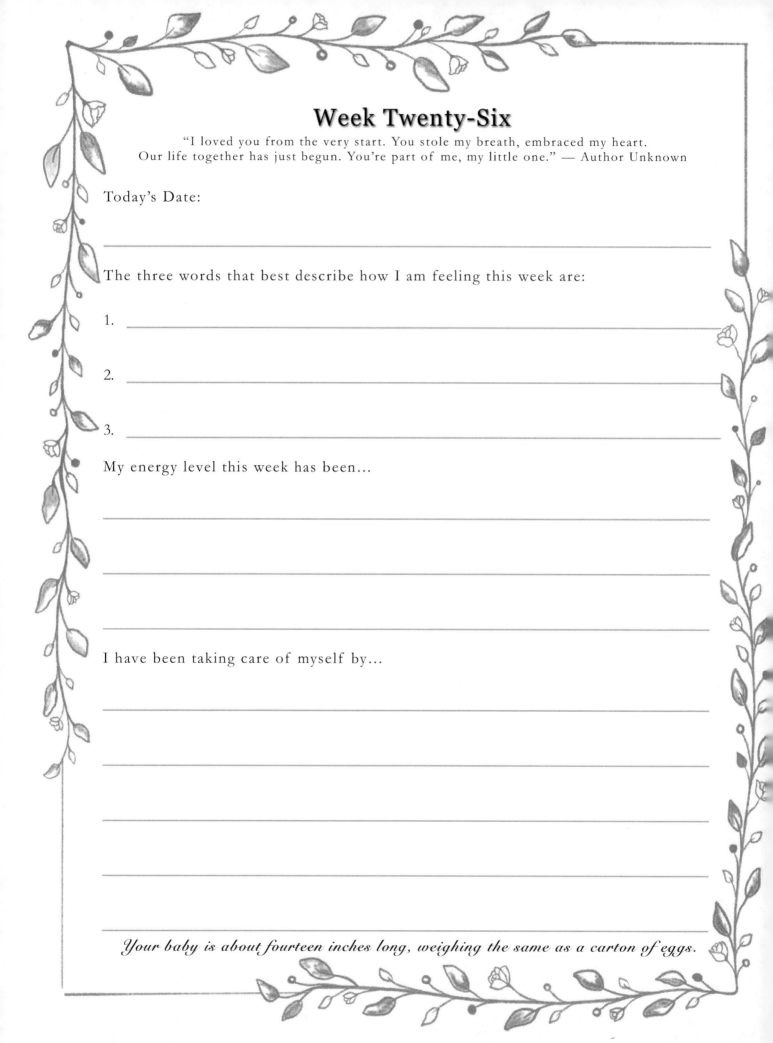

Week Twenty-Six

"I loved you from the very start. You stole my breath, embraced my heart.
Our life together has just begun. You're part of me, my little one." — Author Unknown

Today's Date:

_____

The three words that best describe how I am feeling this week are:

1. _____

2. _____

3. _____

My energy level this week has been...

_____

_____

_____

I have been taking care of myself by...

_____

_____

_____

_____

_____

Your baby is about fourteen inches long, weighing the same as a carton of eggs.

Week Twenty-Six

*"Children have neither past nor future. They enjoy
the present, which very few of us do."* — Jean De La Bruyère

Besides my parents, the person who had the biggest impact on me when I was growing up was...

_____

_____

Their biggest influence on me was...

_____

_____

_____

_____

The main lessons and examples they gave me that I want to give my child include...

_____

_____

_____

_____

_____

Your insurance may pay for a breast pump if you are planning on breastfeeding.

Week Twenty-Six

"The perfect perfume? The smell of a baby of course!"
— Author Unknown

One day, when my baby looks back on their childhood, I want them to remember and think about this the most...

_____

_____

_____

_____

_____

_____

_____

_____

_____

_____

Unless your doctor has said otherwise, continue taking a daily prenatal vitamin.

A Moment for You

"Every 'to-do' list should start with at least one 'for me.'"
— Author Unknown

It probably seems years away from when your baby will be crawling and walking. That said, it will happen before you know it, making NOW a great time to baby proof your house.

Give yourself the gift of peace of mind by spending the week buying-removing-installing-securing-changing the following:

- Survey your entire home and fix anything that could cause injury when climbed on, opened, closed, pulled, pushed, or chewed.
- Install a smoke detector in every room.
- Buy and learn how to use a home fire extinguisher.
- Install a carbon monoxide detector on every floor of your home and in the bedroom hallways.
- Buy and learn how to use a home first-aid kit created for babies.
- Ensure your water heater is not set above 120 degrees Fahrenheit/48 degrees Celsius.
- Pad all furniture corners and secure all furniture to the wall.
- In older homes, ensure the paint isn't lead based.
- Install child-proof latches on all cabinets, pantries, and drawers.
- Install safety plugs in all electrical outlets.
- Remove all blinds and curtains that use a long, looped cord.
- Make a list of emergency contacts and keep it in a location anyone can access.
- Put all key emergency contacts in your cellphone(s). Examples include doctor, closest hospital, and poison control.
- Place nonslip pads under rugs.
- Install baby gates to prevent access to stairs and off-limit rooms.
- Place all medication and cleaning supplies up and out-of-reach.

A longer list can be found by Googling "baby proof your home."

Up to this point, your baby's eyelids have been tightly sealed over their eyes. In week twenty-seven they are now beginning to open.

Week Twenty-Seven

"It is the most powerful creation for you to be able to have life growing inside of you. There is no bigger gift, nothing more empowering." — Beyoncé Knowles

Today's Date:

_____

The three words that best describe how I am feeling this week are:

1. _____

2. _____

3. _____

My energy level this week has been...

_____

_____

_____

I have been taking care of myself by...

_____

_____

_____

_____

They are now a little under fourteen and half inches in length and weighs one pound, nine ounces, the same as your average head of cauliflower.

Week Twenty-Seven

"If you want your children to be intelligent, read them fairy tales. If you want them to be more intelligent, read them more fairy tales." — Albert Einstein

The main things I found myself craving during the second trimester were...

_____

_____

_____

The song that best describes my second trimester is...

_____

_____

Some of my most favorite memories from the second trimester are...

_____

_____

_____

_____

Your baby is practicing breathing by inhaling and exhaling amniotic fluid.

Week Twenty-Seven

"Life began with waking up and loving my mother's face."
— George Washington

Lately, when I find myself anxious or feeling down, it has been about…

_____

_____

_____

_____

_____

_____

When I find myself becoming restless or low, a few of the things I can do to help myself are…

_____

_____

_____

_____

_____

_____

Make sure you are working with your employer to plan your maternity leave.

A Moment for You

"God gave us two hands. One to help others and one to help ourselves."
— Author Unknown

This is the last week of your second trimester, creating the perfect moment to pause and remember all you and your baby have accomplished and to make a list of things you are grateful for.

Gratitude

The practice of gratitude has become a daily activity for many because of the positive impact it can have on our health, mental state, and relationships.

As I approach the third trimester of my pregnancy, I am grateful for...

_____

_____

_____

_____

_____

_____

_____

_____

_____

Your little one has tripled in size since the start of week thirteen.

Notes

Notes

THiRD TRiMESTER

"We cannot
direct the wind,
but we can
adjust the sails."

- Dolly Parton

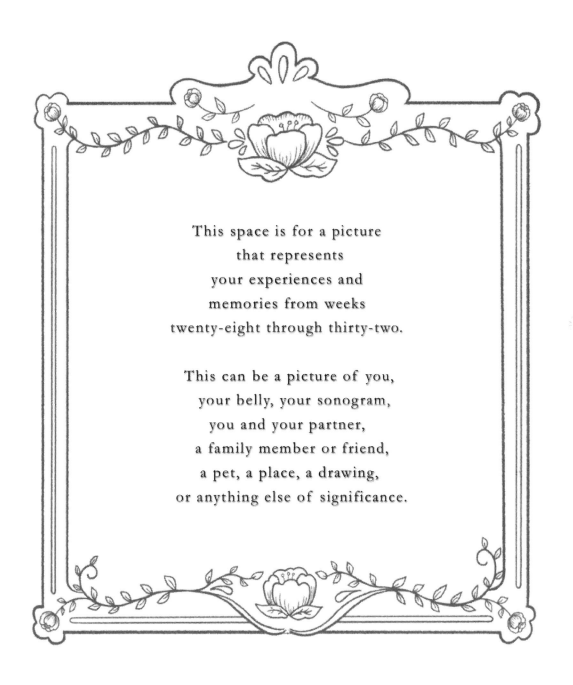

This space is for a picture
that represents
your experiences and
memories from weeks
twenty-eight through thirty-two.

This can be a picture of you,
your belly, your sonogram,
you and your partner,
a family member or friend,
a pet, a place, a drawing,
or anything else of significance.

Weeks 28 to 32

Week Twenty-Eight

"Play is often talked about as if it were a relief from serious learning. But for children play is serious learning. Play is the work of childhood." — Fred Rogers

Today's Date:

_____

The three words that best describe how I am feeling this week are:

1. _____

2. _____

3. _____

My energy level this week has been...

_____

_____

_____

I have been taking care of myself by...

_____

_____

_____

_____

Your baby will blink when light filters in through your womb.

Week Twenty-Eight

"Making the decision to have a child is momentous. It is to decide forever to have your heart go walking around outside your body." — Elizabeth Stone

A letter to myself as I start my third trimester...

_____

_____

_____

_____

_____

_____

_____

_____

_____

_____

_____

Your little one is almost fifteen inches long, the same as an eggplant.

Week Twenty-Eight

"A mother's love endures through all."
— Washington Irving

A letter to my growing baby...

_____

_____

_____

_____

_____

_____

_____

_____

_____

_____

_____

Your baby is experiencing REM sleep, and possibly having dreams.

A Moment for You

"A ruffled mind makes a restless pillow."
— Charlotte Brontë

Your little one's aggressive yoga poses and power kicks may be just a couple of the reasons you are finding it harder to get a full night's sleep. The third trimester is a period when most pregnant women report waking up three or more times during the night.

Some of the other common causes of restless nights include the urge to pee, Braxton Hicks contractions, anxiety, and pain.

Continue to sleep on your left side, using a pregnancy pillow or multiple pillows to keep you in place. Watch your fluid and food intake before bed and avoid caffeine.

If you find yourself awake with a racing mind, get up and do something that is calming. Many find relief from reading, meditating, or writing in a journal.

Relationship Self-Care

One of the many changes that can occur with having a baby is the impact on our friendships.

This makes sense. You suddenly have more to do and more to be concerned with. You mean well and investing time in friendships is on your list of things you want and need to do, but sometimes there just isn't enough time in the day.

Friendships are incredibly important, especially when things are at their craziest. Friends understand and know you in ways others never will. They have known you at your best and at your worst. Equally important, they help keep you connected to where you have been and what you have achieved.

Set aside time this week to spend time with one or more of your close friends. Grab lunch or dinner. Go do a favorite group activity. At a minimum, schedule time for a phone call to catch up and make future plans.

Your doctor will most likely increase the frequency of your check-ups to every two weeks until you enter your 36th week of pregnancy.

Week Twenty-Nine

"A mother is one to whom you hurry when you are troubled."
— Emily Dickinson

Today's Date:

_____

The three words that best describe how I am feeling this week are:

1. _____

2. _____

3. _____

My energy level this week has been...

_____

_____

_____

I have been taking care of myself by...

_____

_____

_____

_____

Your baby will triple in weight from now to week forty.

Week Twenty-Nine

"Children are the bridge to heaven."
— Persian Proverb

Aspects of how I was raised that I want to embrace when raising my own children are...

_____

_____

_____

_____

_____

_____

_____

_____

_____

_____

This is a good time to order a kit if you will be banking your baby's cord blood.

Week Twenty-Nine

"A baby's smile is a bit of sunlight wrapped in your arms."
— Author Unknown

Aspects of how I was raised that I may do differently are...

_____

_____

_____

_____

_____

_____

_____

_____

_____

_____

_____

Your baby is spending about ninety-five percent of their time asleep.

A Moment for You

"For when a child is born, the mother is born again."
— Gilbert Parker

This is a good time to start doing kick counts. Counting your baby's kicks is a fun way to check in and see how they are doing.

The process is simple:

- This is best done while lying down or sitting with your feet up.
- On day one, pick a time when your baby is typically active and you can focus on them.
- Count the number of minutes it takes for you to feel them move ten separate times. A movement is a kick, push, jab, twist, or turn.
- Write the number of minutes down.
- Repeat the above at the same time every day for the next five days, making sure to write down the number of minutes for each day.
- Add up the total number of minutes from all five days and divide that number by five.
- The result is the average length of time it takes for your baby to move or kick ten times, also known as the Kick Count Time.
- On day six and at the same time of day, count the number of minutes it takes for you to feel your baby move ten separate times.
- Compare this number to the Kick Count Time number.
- Do this each day.
- If you notice a big slowing down of how long it takes for your baby to move ten times (when compared to the Kick Count Time), contact your doctor immediately.

Schedule Your Self-Care Time

Sit down and schedule daily self-care time for the next four weeks (weeks twenty-nine through thirty-two). Try for the daily thirty minutes minimum and the extra added hour every week.

In week twenty-nine, your baby weighs almost three pounds and is fifteen and 1/4 inches long, which is the length of a bowling pin.

Week Thirty

"If love is sweet as a flower, then my mother is that sweet flower of love."
— Stevie Wonder

Today's Date:

_____

The three words that best describe how I am feeling this week are:

1. _____

2. _____

3. _____

My energy level this week has been...

_____

_____

_____

I have been taking care of myself by...

_____

_____

_____

_____

Your baby weighs about three pounds and is the size of a large zucchini.

Week Thirty

"Count your age by friends, not years. Count your life by smiles, not tears."
— John Lennon

While being pregnant can be challenging, it is nothing compared to some of the things I have overcome and succeeded at in life. The biggest challenge I have faced in my life was...

_____

_____

_____

_____

_____

Overcoming this challenge made me stronger in the following ways...

_____

_____

_____

_____

_____

Week thirty means ten more weeks to go!

A Moment for You
"Make sure that when you say, 'yes' to others you aren't saying 'no' to yourself."
— Author Unknown

Creating a birth plan provides you the opportunity to contemplate and then define what the ideal birthing experience is for you and your baby.

While things sometimes don't go as planned, it is important to communicate your preferences and desires to the birthing facility and your medical team. Doing so provides you with a feeling of empowerment and control, helps reduce some of the unknown, and helps you focus on yourself and delivering your baby.

Building a Birth Plan
Dream and design your perfect delivery day by building your birth plan.

The next few pages will assist you in considering a variety of options. Use them to create a final list that you can then use to work with your doctor and birthing center to determine what they are able to provide and support.

Start with the big stuff. Where do you want to deliver? Will you be having a vaginal birth, C-Section, water bath delivery, or another option? What level of pain suppression would you like available? Who do you want present before, during, and after you give birth?

What mood and environment would you like in the delivery room? Do you have a song playlist you want to hear? Do you want the lights bright or dimmed?

Is there a specific person you want to cut the umbilical cord? Will you be banking the cord blood? Do you want any pictures or videos taken?

This is your delivery day. Take some time to make it as specific to you and your needs as possible.

In week thirty, your baby may be pressing on your diaphragm, making you short of breath. You can get relief by sleeping semi propped up and by standing throughout the day.

Making Your Birth Plan

"Life is what happens to us while we are making other plans."
— Allen Saunders

My delivery date is:

_____

My doctor's name and contact information are:

_____

My doula's name and contact information are:

_____

During labor, the following people can be present:

_____

_____

_____

_____

_____

_____

_____

Making Your Birth Plan

"Ideas become plans when they are put on paper."
— Author Unknown

My preferred way for my baby to be delivered is:

Vaginal Delivery _____   C-Section _____

Water Delivery _____   Other _____

During labor, if possible, I would like:

☐ To be able to walk around.

☐ To remain in bed.

☐ The use of a delivery tub.

☐ Access to a shower.

☐ Access to a birthing chair.

☐ Access to a birthing stool.

☐ Access to a squatting bar.

☐ An exercise or delivery ball.

☐ This style of music playing:

_____

☐ No music playing.

☐ The room to be as quiet as possible.

☐ Access to a television.

☐ Interruptions to be kept to a minimum.

☐ Hospital staff to be limited to my doctor and nurses (no students, residents, or interns).

☐ To wear clothes that I bring.

☐ To wear my contact lenses during delivery.

☐ To be able to drink approved liquids.

☐ To have access to snacks approved by my doctor.

☐ To have access to my phone.

☐ The lights to be (dimmed or bright): _____

☐ _____

☐ _____

Making Your Birth Plan

"Noah built the ark before it started raining."
— Author Unknown

Photos and videos are:

☐ Allowed

☐ Allowed, but I must be asked first.

☐ Not allowed.

The following must be approved by me:

☐ An IV unless medically necessary.

☐ A saline or heparin lock.

☐ An enema.

☐ Shaving any area of my body.

If my doctor determines during labor that a C-Section is necessary, I would like to be able to discuss the following before the procedure:

_____

_____

_____

_____

_____

_____

_____

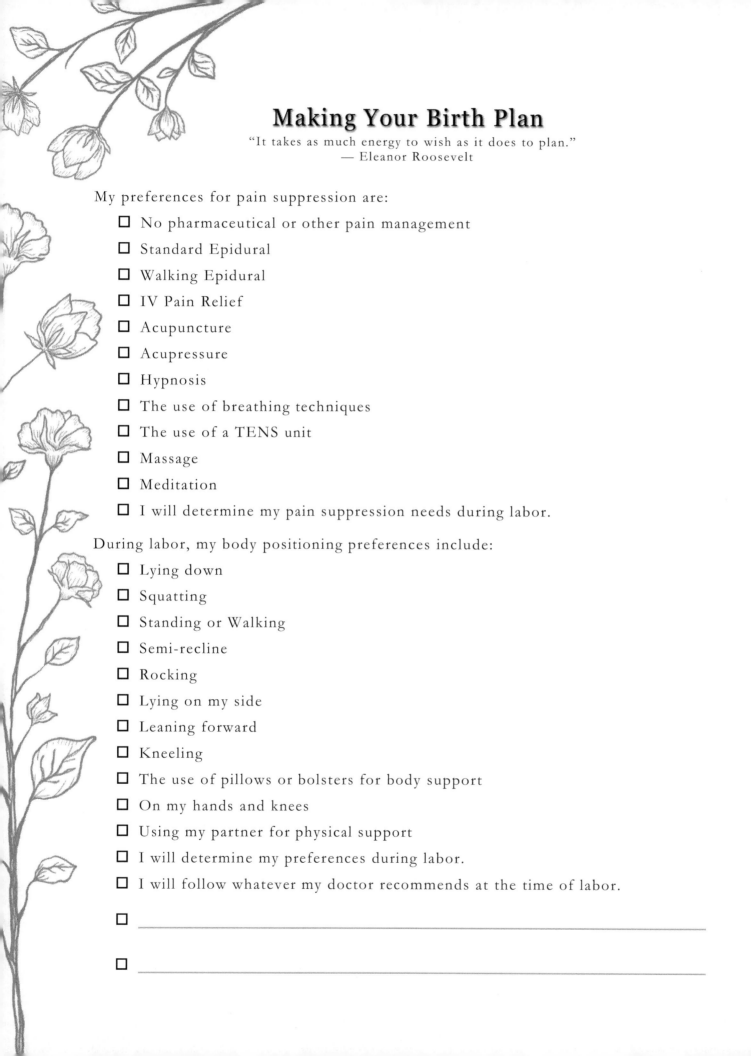

Making Your Birth Plan

"It takes as much energy to wish as it does to plan."
— Eleanor Roosevelt

My preferences for pain suppression are:

☐ No pharmaceutical or other pain management

☐ Standard Epidural

☐ Walking Epidural

☐ IV Pain Relief

☐ Acupuncture

☐ Acupressure

☐ Hypnosis

☐ The use of breathing techniques

☐ The use of a TENS unit

☐ Massage

☐ Meditation

☐ I will determine my pain suppression needs during labor.

During labor, my body positioning preferences include:

☐ Lying down

☐ Squatting

☐ Standing or Walking

☐ Semi-recline

☐ Rocking

☐ Lying on my side

☐ Leaning forward

☐ Kneeling

☐ The use of pillows or bolsters for body support

☐ On my hands and knees

☐ Using my partner for physical support

☐ I will determine my preferences during labor.

☐ I will follow whatever my doctor recommends at the time of labor.

☐ _____

☐ _____

Making Your Birth Plan

"Good fortune is what happens when opportunity meets with planning."
— Thomas Edison

As I am delivering, I would like:

- ☐ To be able to push at my own pace and self-direction.

- ☐ To be coached and directed on when to push.

- ☐ To be able to view my baby being born by using a mirror or video system.
- ☐ To be able to touch my baby's head as it crowns.

- ☐ For my partner to be able to touch the baby's head as it crowns.

- ☐ To avoid any sort of birthing assistance, such as forceps or vacuum extraction.

If an episiotomy is required, my preferences are:

- ☐ To first use perineal massage and body positioning to avoid the need for an episiotomy.
- ☐ For an episiotomy to only occur if during labor my doctor determines it is necessary to avoid perineal tearing.
- ☐ If one is needed, my preference is that a pressure episiotomy be used (this is when the doctor waits until the head is crowning and makes an incision that is minimal in length.)
- ☐ If an episiotomy is needed, my preference is that a local anesthetic be used.
- ☐ If an episiotomy is needed, my preference is that no local anesthetic be used.

After my baby is delivered, I would like:

- ☐ This person to cut the umbilical cord:

_____

- ☐ To bank the cord blood (Parentsguidecordblood.org/en is a great resource for questions.)
- ☐ To donate my baby's cord blood.
- ☐ To deliver the placenta naturally.
- ☐ To save the placenta.
- ☐ The use of Oxytocin/Pitocin only if medically necessary.

- ☐ _____

- ☐ _____

- ☐ _____

Making Your Birth Plan

"A goal without a plan is just a wish." — Author Unknown

After I deliver, I would like to:

☐ Hold my baby immediately.

☐ Hold them after they have been weighed and suctioned.

☐ Hold them after they have been cleaned.

My preferences for feeding my baby are:

☐ To breastfeed as soon as possible after delivery.

☐ To use formula.

☐ To be determined after delivery.

After delivery, the following people can visit me and our baby:

_____

_____

_____

_____

_____

_____

_____

_____

Making Your Birth Plan

"Plans are roadmaps to your chosen destination." — Toni Story

Additional preferences, items, and notes...

Week Thirty-One

"You can learn many things from children. How much patience you have, for instance." — Franklin P. Adams

Today's Date:

_____

The three words that best describe how I am feeling this week are:

1. _____

2. _____

3. _____

My energy level this week has been...

_____

_____

_____

I have been taking care of myself by...

_____

_____

_____

_____

_____

Your rapidly growing baby weighs three and a third pounds, the same as a coconut.

Week Thirty-One

*"No matter how bad my day has been, it takes one little
kick to make everything feel alright."* — Author Unknown

This is how I imagine my life will be six months after my baby is born...

_____

_____

_____

_____

_____

_____

_____

_____

_____

_____

Only use a brand-new car seat. Used ones can be defective or damaged.

Week Thirty-One

"Everything grows rounder and wider and weirder, and I sit here in the middle of it all and wonder who in the world you will turn out to be." — Carrie Fisher

And this is how I imagine my life will be when my baby turns eighteen...

_____

_____

_____

_____

_____

_____

_____

_____

_____

_____

Be sure to review how to help your pets relax with a new baby in the house.

A Moment for You

"You yourself, as much as anybody in the entire universe, deserve your love and affection." — Buddha

The rumours are true: the first few weeks with a new baby take a lot out of you.

There won't be enough sleep. Your emotions will be on a continuous roller coaster. Your home's walls will seem to grow closer, and every inch of space will be taken over by all things baby.

A way to manage some of the resulting stress is to give yourself a space that is just for you. Creating a refuge will give you the feeling of being able to escape and relax, even if it is just for a few minutes tucked away in a back room.

It can be as simple as a favorite chair in a corner of a quiet room. Surround it with things that comfort you: a scented candle, a favorite book, fresh flowers, photographs... Tell yourself that time in this spot is time for you. Create a ritual when you sit here, such as sipping tea or writing in your journal or anything else that helps you pause.

An area in my home that I could turn into a "My Space" place is...

_____

A few things I could add to this spot to help it be calming and relaxing are...

_____

_____

_____

_____

_____

Remember that just five percent of all births make it to the predicted due date.

Week Thirty-Two

"Mother is the name for God in the lips and hearts of little children."
— William Makepeace Thackeray

Today's Date:

_____

The three words that best describe how I am feeling this week are:

1. _____

2. _____

3. _____

My energy level this week has been...

_____

_____

_____

I have been taking care of myself by...

_____

_____

_____

_____

Your baby weighs about four pounds, the same as a whole pound cake.

Week Thirty-Two

"A child's love could simply be one of the most beautiful sounds in the world."
— Author Unknown

When I think about going into labor, I find myself anxious or fearful about...

_____

_____

_____

_____

_____

I can help ease these worries and fears by doing a few of the following things...

_____

_____

_____

_____

_____

Your baby is beginning to move themselves into a head down position.

Week Thirty-Two

"In time of test, family is best."
— Burmese Proverb

A letter to myself to reassure me and soothe my worries about labor...

_____

_____

_____

_____

_____

_____

_____

_____

_____

_____

_____

Most doctors will do your Group B Strep test in weeks thirty-five to thirty-seven.

A Moment for You

"When you make your soul happy, you make heaven happy."
— Persian Proverb

If this is your first baby, it is difficult to fully describe the highs and lows you will experience in the first few months after you give birth.

The best way to describe it may be to tell you it will be one of the most joyous and exciting times of your life, but it will require a herculean exertion through seemingly endless days, minimal sleep, messy rooms, constant feedings, and diaper changes, and delivered food.

Planning now for the first weeks of life with your new baby can help make this period a little easier.

Sit down with your partner and create a post-partum plan for the first six to eight weeks of life post-delivery.

A few good things to make agreements on and plan:

- **Visitors:** who might visit, what times of the day would work best for you and your baby, and a loose guideline on the length of visits.
- **Meals:** do you want to cook ahead and freeze meals, order out, or stock the house with easy-to-prepare items? You can also think about asking close family and friends to bring a meal over when they visit. Also be sure to stock the house with your go-to foods and beverages.
- **Household chores:** who does what and how often? Make a plan for all common chores, like shopping, laundry, taking out the trash, picking up common areas, and taking care of other children and/or pets. This can help avoid the stress, tension, and conflict that a cluttered house can create.
- **Emergency contacts:** put together a list of important names and numbers (doctor, closest hospital, etc.) and key family and friends. Post this list in a place easily accessible to everyone.
- **Scheduled downtime:** be sure to talk about and designate how you can both get that much needed rest or alone time during these first crazy weeks.

While getting to full term is important, the good news is that the overwhelming majority of babies born from this point forward does not have any long-term issues.

I loved you

before

I knew you.

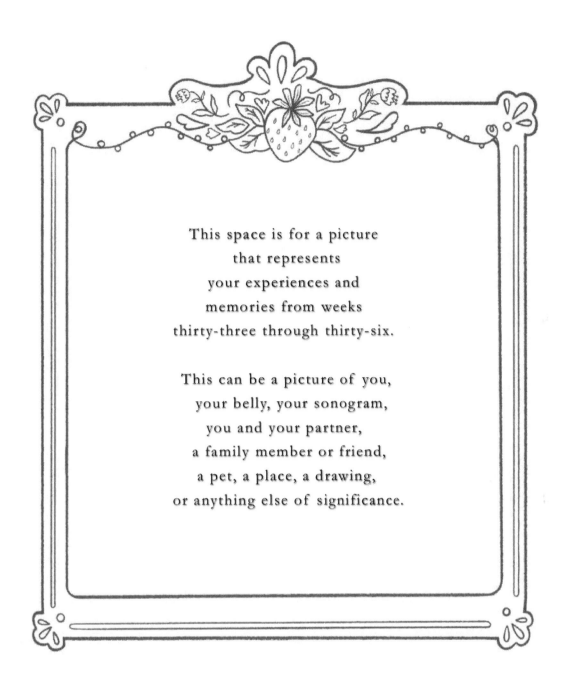

This space is for a picture
that represents
your experiences and
memories from weeks
thirty-three through thirty-six.

This can be a picture of you,
your belly, your sonogram,
you and your partner,
a family member or friend,
a pet, a place, a drawing,
or anything else of significance.

Weeks 33 to 36

Week Thirty-Three

"Whether your pregnancy was meticulously planned, medically coaxed, or happened by surprise, one thing is certain – your life will never be the same." — Catherine Jones

Today's Date:

_____

The three words that best describe how I am feeling this week are:

1. _____

2. _____

3. _____

My energy level this week has been...

_____

_____

_____

I have been taking care of myself by...

_____

_____

_____

_____

Your baby's increase in weight is making their skin less wrinkled and smoother.

Week Thirty-Three

"Childbirth is more admirable than conquest, more amazing than self-defence, and as courageous as either one." — Gloria Steinem

The best advice I was given about being pregnant was...

_____

_____

_____

_____

The most memorable thing someone has told me about being pregnant is...

_____

_____

_____

_____

_____

Contact your health insurance provider about adding your newborn to your policy.

Week Thirty-Three

"I'm a mother, and I look like one."
— Olivia Wilde

One thing I wish someone had told me about being pregnant is...

_____

_____

_____

_____

_____

Of all the things I have been told about having a baby, the one that I hope to never hear again is...

_____

_____

_____

_____

_____

Your baby now has a working immune system.

A Moment for You

"It is not the load that breaks you down. It's the way you carry it."
— Lena Horne

Self-Care Schedule Time!
Take out your planner and schedule daily time over the next eight weeks (weeks thirty-three through forty).

That's right, you only have eight more weeks until your due date.

Try for a minimum of thirty minutes each day but give yourself as much as you can. Delivery day is just around the corner, and you are going to need (and deserve!) extra care and extra rest.

Braxton Hicks Contractions
This is also the time when many women begin to experience Braxton Hicks contractions. These painless tightening sensations are your uterus "practicing" for the big delivery day.

Braxton Hicks contractions can last about fifteen to thirty seconds and occur in random and irregular patterns. Changing your position will often make them go away.

Regular "real" contractions occur in regular intervals and grow stronger, last longer, and are closer together as you get closer to labor.

More Firsts
The first time I felt my baby kick was...

_____

My reaction was...

_____

_____

The first person (besides me) to feel my baby kick was...

_____

Your baby has grown more than an inch since last week and now weighs between four and five pounds, about the same as a spaghetti squash.

Week Thirty-Four

"A mother's love for her child is like nothing else in the world."
— Author Unknown

Today's Date:

_____

The three words that best describe how I am feeling this week are:

1. _____

2. _____

3. _____

My energy level this week has been...

_____

_____

_____

I have been taking care of myself by...

_____

_____

_____

_____

_____

Your baby now weighs five pounds, the same as a bag of flour.

Week Thirty-Four

"To understand your parents' love, you must raise children yourself."
— Chinese Proverb

Being pregnant has inspired me to...

_____

_____

_____

_____

_____

Being pregnant has taught me...

_____

_____

_____

_____

_____

Remember to schedule someone to care for any children or pets on delivery day.

Week Thirty-Four

"A mother's heart is a baby's most beautiful dwelling."
— Author Unknown

Self-care is us saying to ourselves, "I Love You." This is a letter of love I have written to myself...

_____

_____

_____

_____

_____

_____

_____

_____

_____

_____

*Thirty-four weeks means you are in your
eighth month (give or take) of pregnancy.*

A Moment for You

"I celebrate myself, and sing myself."
— Walt Whitman

Week thirty-four means you are seven weeks away from your due date.

This is a good week to start packing a bag to take with you to the birthing center/hospital. Preparing now will give you some extra peace of mind and a little more time to relax and rest in the final weeks of your pregnancy.

The first question of packing is typically, "How long will I be staying?"

Typical hospital stays after delivering a baby are one to two days for an uncomplicated delivery and three to four for a cesarean section. Also, just to play it safe, go ahead and plan for an extra night or two if yours is considered a "high-risk" pregnancy. Always better to be prepared!

The second question is, "What do I need to pack?"

The next few pages include a checklist of items for yourself, for your partner, and for your new baby. In the spirit of keeping things simple and easy, the list focuses on the basics.

The third question is, "What kind of bag should I bring?"

Keep it minimal in size but big enough to accommodate what you are bringing. A good size bag is a typical weekender.

Don't worry or stress over what you are or aren't bringing. Forgotten items can be retrieved and most hospitals often have a supply of toiletries and baby items they can give you.

Ask your hospital what is provided for new mothers and babies so you can remove those items from your packing list.

Birthing Bag Checklist

"That first pregnancy is a long sea journey to a country where you don't know the language, and where land is in sight for such a long time." — Emily Perkins

- ☐ Pajamas
- ☐ Slippers
- ☐ Warm Socks
- ☐ Sweater/Warm Top
- ☐ Robe
- ☐ Nursing Bra
- ☐ Underwear
- ☐ Clothes to Wear Home
- ☐ Contact Lenses/Glasses
- ☐ Contact Lens Solution
- ☐ Toothbrush
- ☐ Toothpaste
- ☐ Deodorant
- ☐ Shampoo
- ☐ Hairbrush
- ☐ Hair Ties
- ☐ Makeup
- ☐ Insurance Card
- ☐ Driver's License/ID
- ☐ Pediatrician Contact Information
- ☐ Birth Plan
- ☐ Baby Blanket
- ☐ Baby Clothes

- ☐ _____
- ☐ _____
- ☐ _____

Birthing Bag Checklist

"For this child, I prayed, and the Lord has
granted the desires of my heart." — 1 Samuel 1:27

- ☐ Swaddle
- ☐ Nursing Cover
- ☐ Snacks
- ☐ Birthing Ball (if using)
- ☐ Music (if desired)
- ☐ Camera (if desired)
- ☐ Essential Oils (if desired)
- ☐ Car Seat
- ☐ Belly Band (if using)
- ☐ Book
- ☐ Computer Tablet (if desired)
- ☐ Charging Cords
- ☐ _____
- ☐ _____
- ☐ _____
- ☐ _____
- ☐ _____
- ☐ _____
- ☐ _____
- ☐ _____
- ☐ _____
- ☐ _____

Week Thirty-Five

"A baby's kick is just a hug from the inside."
— Author Unknown

Today's Date:

_____

The three words that best describe how I am feeling this week are:

1. _____

2. _____

3. _____

My energy level this week has been...

_____

_____

_____

I have been taking care of myself by...

_____

_____

_____

_____

Be sure to confirm your maternity leave plans with your employer.

Week Thirty-Five

"No matter your age, you will always need your mom."
— Author Unknown

To me, being a successful parent means...

_____

_____

_____

_____

The person I consider to be the ultimate parenting superstar is...

_____

_____

They are an amazing parent because of these qualities...

_____

_____

_____

_____

_____

_____

This is a good week to visit your hairdresser one last time before delivery day.

Week Thirty-Five

"A mother's arms are more comforting than anyone else's!"
— Princess Diana

The thing that most excites me about being a parent is...

_____

_____

_____

_____

_____

The thing that scares me the most about being a parent is...

_____

_____

_____

_____

_____

The amount of amniotic fluid surrounding your baby is starting to lessen.

A Moment for You

This Week's Act of Self-Care
The end of week thirty-five means you are five weeks away from your due date.

Getting your maximum level of rest now will go a long way to getting you ready for the quickly approaching days and nights of taking care of a newborn. This is a good time to start handing off one or two or more household duties.

An excellent treat to give yourself is to hire a professional house cleaner to do a full cleaning before the baby arrives. In addition to giving you a much needed and deserved break, you will also gain some extra peace of mind knowing you are bringing your brand-new baby home to a freshly cleaned house.

If it fits your budget, hire a service to come in a few weeks before your delivery to do a thorough deep cleaning. This level of service includes the standard activities of vacuuming, mopping, dusting, and cleaning bathrooms, but adds harder to clean areas like getting behind appliances, cleaning windows and baseboards, scrubbing down the oven, wiping down cabinets, and removing the calcium and scale build-up that accumulates on faucets and taps.

More Firsts
The first time I couldn't wear my usual shoes was...

_____

The first time I couldn't see my feet was...

_____

_____

The first time I needed a little help getting up was...

_____

_____

Your baby is about eighteen inches long, about the size of a pineapple.

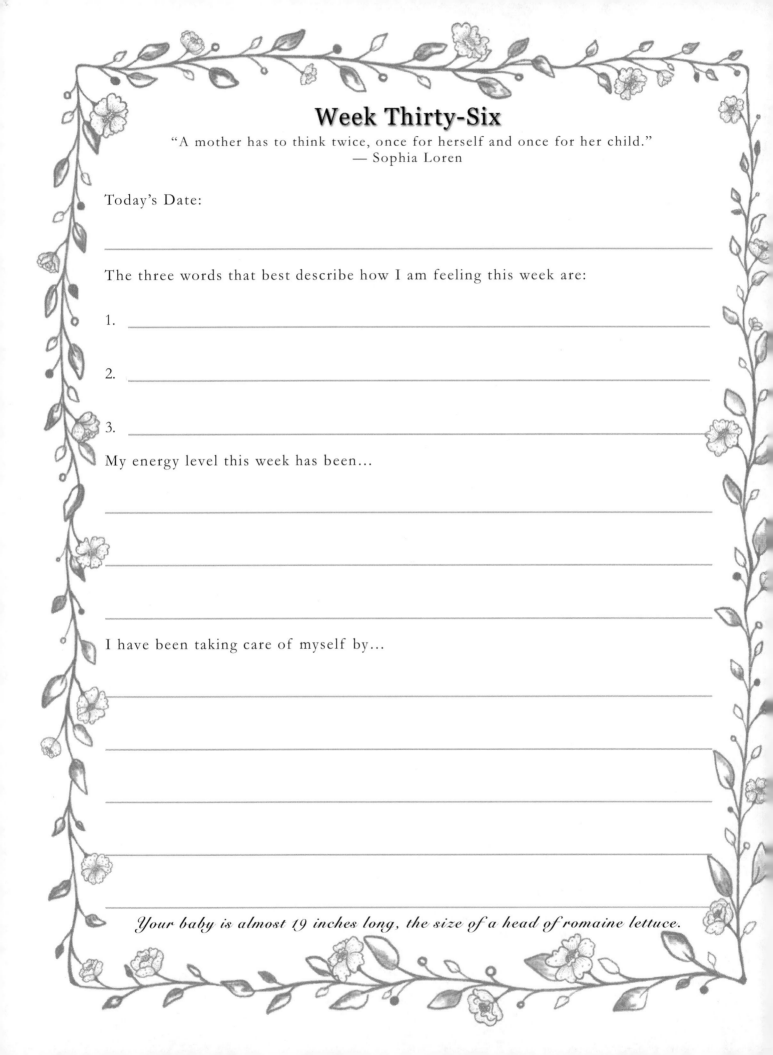

Week Thirty-Six

"A mother has to think twice, once for herself and once for her child."
— Sophia Loren

Today's Date:

_____

The three words that best describe how I am feeling this week are:

1. _____

2. _____

3. _____

My energy level this week has been...

_____

_____

_____

I have been taking care of myself by...

_____

_____

_____

_____

Your baby is almost 19 inches long, the size of a head of romaine lettuce.

Week Thirty-Six

"Sometimes I open my mouth and my mother comes out."
— Bridgette Canton

Being a part of a family means this to me...

_____

_____

_____

_____

Out of everyone in my extended family, the person I am closest with is...

_____

_____

The family relationship that I want to work on or heal is...

_____

_____

One way I can start the process of reconnecting with this person is...

_____

_____

Starting in week thirty-six, your doctor visits may increase to once a week.

Week Thirty-Six

"Even miracles take a little time."
— Eula Mason

When I imagine what my family and homelife looks like in ten years, this is what I dream...

_____

_____

_____

_____

_____

_____

_____

_____

_____

_____

This week begins a period of rapid weight gain for your baby with them gaining another two to five pounds by week forty.

A Moment for You

"Of course, I am tired. I am carrying an entire world inside me."
— Author Unknown

This Week's Act of Self-Care

As the big day gets closer, let's keep focusing on how to increase peace of mind for self-care. The correct installation and use of a rear-facing infant car seat is one of the most critical ways to protect the life and safety of your baby.

Key things to know when buying and using an infant car seat are:

- Read your car's owner's manual to determine if there are any special requirements and to understand how to install.
- Focus on seats made especially for infants.
- Make sure it is made with materials that are easy to clean.
- Only use seats that meet National Highway Traffic Safety Administration and American Association of Pediatrics standards.
- Read the product label and instructions to understand its height, weight, and age limits.
- The safest car seat is the one that correctly fits your child's age, height, and weight, AND fits and is compatible with your vehicle, AND is correctly installed.
- The safest place to install an infant's car seat is in the back seat facing backwards, using a five-point harness system.
- A five-point harness system secures your infant with straps that run across the shoulders and hips and secure between the legs.
- Never install a car seat where an airbag is active and could be deployed.
- When installing, read and follow the car seat manual carefully and precisely. This is not a time for guessing or shortcuts.
- Your local police or fire station will happily inspect your installation for free. You can also find a local inspector at: **cert.safekids.org/get-car-seat-checked**
- Never use a second-hand infant car seat as it may have been previously damaged or have been subject of a product recall.
- Any car seat that was in the car when a collision occurred should be replaced. This applies even if the seat shows no signs of damage.

Your baby's brain is currently growing at an incredible rate, tripling in how much it weighs during the third trimester.

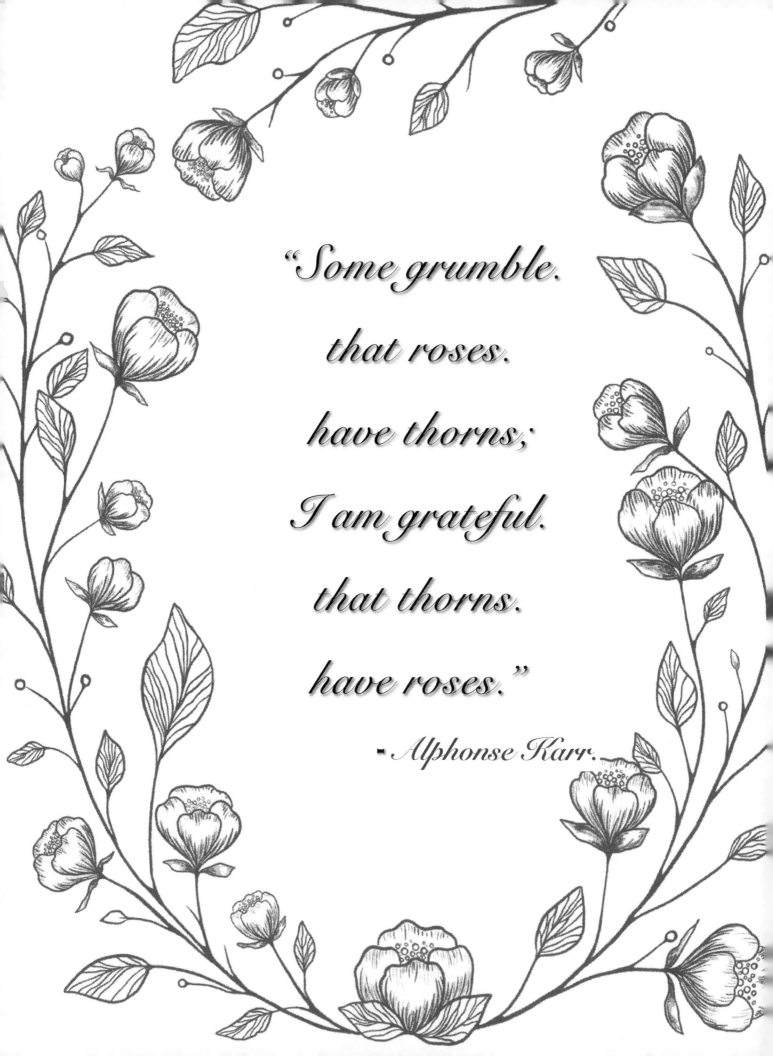

"Some grumble.

that roses.

have thorns;

I am grateful.

that thorns.

have roses."

- Alphonse Karr.

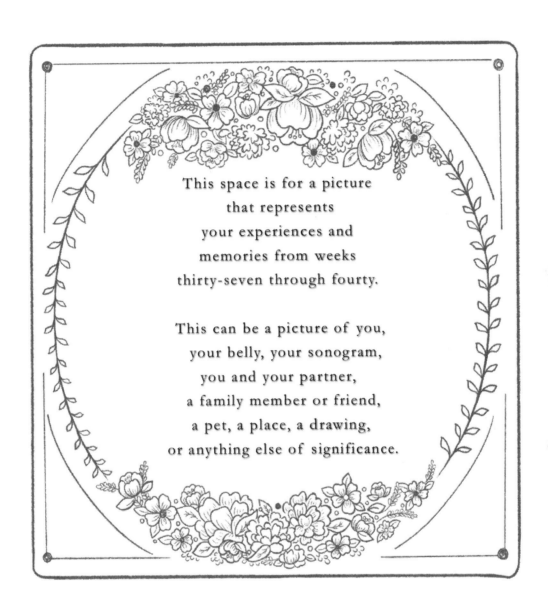

This space is for a picture
that represents
your experiences and
memories from weeks
thirty-seven through fourty.

This can be a picture of you,
your belly, your sonogram,
you and your partner,
a family member or friend,
a pet, a place, a drawing,
or anything else of significance.

Weeks 37 to 40

Week Thirty-Seven

"Little souls find their way to you whether they're from your womb or someone else's." — Sheryl Crow

Today's Date:

_____

The three words that best describe how I am feeling this week are:

1. _____

2. _____

3. _____

My energy level this week has been...

_____

_____

_____

I have been taking care of myself by...

_____

_____

_____

_____

_____

Three more weeks to week forty!

Week Thirty-Seven

"Only mothers can think of the future – because they give birth to it in their children." — Maxim Gorky

The people I need to ensure are notified when my baby is born are...

_____

_____

_____

_____

_____

_____

_____

_____

_____

_____

Have you finalized your selection of a pediatrician for your new baby?

Week Thirty-Seven

"My daughter introduced me to myself."
— Beyoncé Knowles

The people I need to ensure are notified when my baby is born are...

Create a group text or email with everyone you want to notify once your baby is born. This will simplify things and help you not forget anyone.

A Moment for You

"When the well's dry, we know the worth of water."
— Benjamin Franklin

Three weeks until your due date!

You may begin to feel pelvic pressure and occasional discomfort as your baby moves into position for delivery. You can give yourself some relief by sitting with your feet raised, resting on your side, or by wearing a pelvic support belt.

A Little Preparation Goes a Long Way

This is a good week to make sure a few basics are ready to go for the big day:

1. Do a final review and print a few copies of your birth plan.
2. Did you preregister at the hospital or birthing center? Doing so will make delivery day smoother and easier and help avoid later issues with insurance and billing.
3. Do a final check to make sure your hospital bag is packed and ready to go. Make sure to include a copy of your birth plan in there.
4. Make sure your partner's hospital bag is packed. Insert a copy of your birth plan there as well.
5. Verify any arrangements you have made for someone to take care of your children or pets.
6. Install your infant car seat and make sure your car has a full tank/charge.
7. Verify you have a good supply of diapers, wipes, and baby clothes on hand.
8. Have your partner do a few loads of laundry.
9. Verify your list of people you want to be notified when you have the baby.
10. Verify you have your doctor's contact information in an accessible location.
11. Do a few practice drives to the hospital/birthing center. How long does it take? Is their heavy traffic at certain times of the day?
12. Rest.
13. Rest some more.
14. And then take a nap.

Your baby is around nineteen inches long, the size of a big stalk of kale.

Week Thirty-Eight

"If I know what love is, it's because of you."
— Hermann Hesse

Today's Date:

_____

The three words that best describe how I am feeling this week are:

1. _____

2. _____

3. _____

My energy level this week has been...

_____

_____

_____

I have been taking care of myself by...

_____

_____

_____

_____

_____

Your baby is now about twenty inches long and around seven pounds in weight. About the size of a mini watermelon.

Week Thirty-Eight

"Mothers hold their children's hands for a short while, but their hearts forever."
— Author Unknown

Much of the focus of the past eight months has been on my pregnancy and my baby. This week is a good time to focus on me, the individual.

I am happiest when...

_____

_____

_____

_____

_____

I feel in control and most powerful when...

_____

_____

_____

_____

Contact your doctor immediately if you notice sudden swelling in your face, hands, or feet, as these are signs of possible preeclampsia.

Week Thirty-Eight

"By far the most common craving of pregnant women is not to be pregnant."
— Phyllis Diller

I have strongly developed these talents and skills...

_____

_____

_____

_____

_____

My past self would be proud of current me for these accomplishments...

_____

_____

_____

_____

_____

_____

You may not know your baby's true eye color until they reach one year in age.

Week Thirty-Eight

"Pregnancy is an endless wait followed by an endless love."
— Author Unknown

I am passionate about...

_____

_____

_____

_____

I make a great friend and partner because...

_____

_____

_____

The biggest goal I want to accomplish in the next five years is...

_____

_____

_____

Not that you need a reminder, but delivery day is only two weeks away!

Week Thirty-Eight

"Flowers are words which even a baby can understand."
— Arthur C. Cox

While I am more excited than I ever imagined I could be to be my baby's mom, it is important to also make room in my future life for my needs, my relationships, and my dreams.

After my baby is born, I will do the following to support a life that has room for me as a parent, me as a friend, me as a partner, and me as a person with my own needs and dreams...

_____

_____

_____

_____

_____

_____

_____

_____

_____

Your baby is shedding the fine hair called lanugo
that has covered them since the fourth month.

A Moment for You

In the last few weeks of pregnancy, many moms-to-be experience the sudden urge to organize and clean their home. Known as "nesting," it is common to find oneself getting caught up in making the home ready for the newcomer. Don't worry if you find yourself cleaning out the refrigerator and organizing the junk drawer at two o'clock in the morning.

Just make sure your flurry of activity doesn't include climbing, lifting, or anything else that will strain you or your baby. Avoid caustic cleaning solutions and heavy fumes if you find yourself scrubbing down the oven or bathroom.

If you are feeling the need to "nest," here's a productive list of things you can do that will help you prepare for delivery day and the first few weeks with your new baby:

- Cook and freeze meals for the future.
- Organize your food pantry and refrigerator to get an idea of what you have on hand and what you may need for the next month.
- Stock up on food, toiletries, and other essential items now so you don't have to worry about them during the tiring days of newborn baby care.
- Get caught up on laundry.
- Organize your baby changing area to make diaper time smoother.
- Has your baby's car seat been properly installed in the car you will be taking to the hospital?
- Are there any areas that still need to be baby-proofed?

The nesting urge can also strike your partner, so take advantage and get a few of those long-needed projects completed.

Just make sure you are getting your rest. The next six to eight weeks are going to require a lot of you and now is the time to reserve energy.

Thirty-nine weeks is considered a "full-term" pregnancy. This means this week is a good time to review and understand the signs of labor.

Week Thirty-Nine

"Being a mom is the answer to every question. She is our why. She is our who. She is our what. And she is our when." — Author Unknown

Today's Date:

_____

The three words that best describe how I am feeling this week are:

1. _____

2. _____

3. _____

My energy level this week has been...

_____

_____

_____

I have been taking care of myself by...

_____

_____

_____

_____

Your baby weighs between seven and eight pounds, the size of a pumpkin.

Week Thirty-Nine

"Months have an average of 30 days, except the 9th month of pregnancy, which has about 1,000 days." — Author Unknown

The song that best describes my third trimester is...

_____

_____

_____

The main things I found myself craving during the third trimester were...

_____

_____

_____

The most challenging part of my third trimester was...

_____

_____

_____

_____

Your baby's eyes can see things up to eight inches away.

Week Thirty-Nine

"If pregnancy were a book, they would cut the last two chapters."
— Nora Ephron

A few of my favorite memories from the third trimester are...

_____

_____

_____

_____

_____

_____

_____

_____

_____

_____

Remember that less than five percent of all babies are born on their due date.

A Moment for You

"Fairy tales do come true. Look at us, we had you."
— Author Unknown

It is week thirty-nine and your baby is officially "full-term." Let the countdown begin!

Carrying and growing your little one has been an empowering journey that has led you to this moment, just days away from a new life. There is an excitement and eagerness but also a level of fear and worry.

These mixed-up emotions and feelings make sense and are normal. Try to focus on all you have learned and all your preparation. You're ready.

During this last week of pregnancy, you may be feeling more and more uncomfortable as you manage the usual pregnancy symptoms of fatigue, heartburn, and insomnia. You may also be dealing with an increase in pain and pressure on your back and pelvis as they bear the weight of your almost fully-developed baby.

You may also be experiencing more frequent Braxton Hicks contractions as your body prepares itself for delivery.

If the Braxton Hicks contractions become too uncomfortable, you may gain some relief by changing your position, taking a warm (not hot) bath, drinking a warm drink, or going for a walk. Many get relief with relaxation exercises such as meditation, deep breathing, or focusing their thoughts on something pleasant.

Make sure you stay hydrated and avoid any strenuous activity.

A Final Check

Take this time to confirm that your hospital bags are packed, your birth plan is complete and printed, and you have the directions to the hospital/birthing center.

Verify your arrangements of who will be taking care of any children or pets.

Read up on and make sure you have a clear understanding of the first signs of labor.

Most of all, get as much rest as you can and never forget that *you are ready*.

During this last week, babies typically add a half-pound to one pound in weight with most of the development occurring with the lungs and brain.

Week Forty

"Just when you think you know love, something little comes along and reminds you just how big it is." — Author Unknown

Today's Date:

_____

The three words that best describe how I am feeling this week are:

1. _____

2. _____

3. _____

My energy level this week has been...

_____

_____

_____

I have been taking care of myself by...

_____

_____

_____

_____

_____

Rest. Rest some more. And then rest even more. (You will be glad you did.)

Week Forty

"What lies behind us and what lies before us are tiny matters compared to what lies within us." — Ralph Waldo Emerson

A letter to myself as I come to the end of my pregnancy...

_____

_____

_____

_____

_____

_____

_____

_____

_____

_____

_____

Your baby will likely weigh between six and nine pounds if born this week.

Week Forty

"To give birth is to participate in creation."
— Author Unknown

A letter to my new baby...

_____

_____

_____

_____

_____

_____

_____

_____

_____

_____

_____

Forty weeks means you have reached the nine-month mark!

A Moment for You

"Take rest; a field that has rested gives a bountiful crop!"
— Ovid

There are several indicators that will let you know that labor has started or is about to start and you should head to the hospital:

- You lose your mucus plug. This clear (but sometimes yellow or brown) sticky substance has been protecting your growing baby from the outside world by sealing off your cervix. Losing your mucus plug is followed by a pink or reddish discharge.
- You have begun to experience "real" contractions that can be identified because:
- They become stronger, more painful, and increase in frequency as time progresses.
- The pain is especially noticeable in your back and lower abdomen.
- They may feel like they move from the top of your uterus to the bottom.
- They become longer in duration, often anywhere from thirty to seventy seconds.
- They typically follow a specific pattern in their occurrence.
- Changing your body position or using relaxation exercises does not provide any relief.
- While the majority of women don't experience it, having your water break is also a great sign your baby is on their way.

You Are Ready

- You have been a part of many amazing things over the last thirty-nine weeks.
- Delivering your baby is the last piece in the beginning of your whole new life.

You've got this!
You are ready!

The next few months are going to demand a lot from you, so continue to schedule your time for you. Taking care of yourself will make this new world of taking care of your baby more approachable, more manageable, and most importantly, a tiny bit easier and a whole lot more fun.

*Acknowledge all the incredible work you have done
and tell yourself that you are ready for this next journey.*

The Story of Meeting You

"A wish was made, and you appeared."
— Author Unknown

I went into labor...

On this date:

_____

At this time:

_____

And at this place:

_____

I thought I might be going into labor because...

_____

_____

_____

When I realized I was going into labor, my first reaction and emotions were...

_____

_____

_____

The Story of Meeting You

"How can such tiny feet leave such large footprints in my heart."
— Author Unknown

When I went into labor, I was with...

My story of the trip to where my baby was born is...

The Story of Meeting You

"Your first breath took mine away."
— Author Unknown

My baby was born...

On this date: _____

At this time: _____

And at this place: _____

I was in labor this long: _____

While I was in labor, I was with...

_____

_____

_____

The first time I held my baby, my reaction and emotions were...

_____

_____

_____

_____

The Story of Meeting You

"I don't know who you'll be, but I know you will be my everything."
— Author Unknown

The story of having my baby is...

_____

_____

_____

_____

_____

_____

_____

_____

_____

_____

Notes

Notes

Prenatal Appointments

"I don't know why they say, 'You have a baby.'
The baby has you." — Gallagher

Date: _____

Date: _____

Date: _____

Date: _____

Date: _____

Date: _____

Date: _____

Date: _____

Prenatal Appointments

"When a baby is born, a life of endless
possibilities lies ahead." — Author Unknown

Date: _____

Date: _____

Date: _____

Date: _____

Date: _____

Date: _____

Date: _____

Date: _____

Who Came to My Baby Shower?

Who Came to My Baby Shower?

Thank You to Our Contributors

This book was written with the guidance, help, and consultation of many, including medical professionals, mothers, and a few moms-to-be. All my gratitude for their knowledge, insight, and collaboration - thank you, thank you."

Jeffrey Mason has spent twenty-plus years working with individuals, couples, and organizations to create change, achieve goals, and strengthen relationships.

He begins with the understanding that being human is hard and every person has an amazing life story to share.

He would be grateful if you would help people to find his books by leaving a review on Amazon. Your feedback also helps him get better at this thing he loves.

You can contact him at <u>HearYourStory.com</u> or directly at hello@jeffreymason.com. He would love to hear from you.

Cheryl Olsen's long experience in maternity education and supporting expectant moms-to-be was invaluable in the writing of this book.

Cover illustrations by CK Reed.
CK lives & works in Los Angeles as an artist, illustrator, graphic designer, muralist, art director, and set designer. She has been featured in Surface Magazine and Shoutout LA.

Her work can be viewed at **ckreed.com**.

Interior illustrations by Maria Orlandi.
Maria works in marketing and advertising, and as a freelance illustrator and visual designer. Her art focuses on revealing the beauty of the world around us and exploring the comforting simplicity of nature.

Available at Amazon, all bookstores, and HearYourStory.com

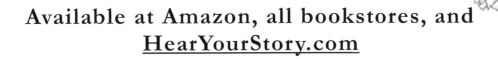

At **Hear Your Story**, we have created a line of books focused on giving each of us a place to tell the unique story of who we are, where we have been, and where we are going.

Sharing and hearing the stories of the people in our lives creates closeness and understanding, ultimately strengthening our bonds.

- Dad, I Want to Hear Your Story; A Father's Guided Journal to Share His Life & His Love

- Mom, I Want to Hear Your Story; A Mother's Guided Journal to Share Her Life & Her Love

- You Choose to Be My Dad; I Want to Hear Your Story: A Guided Journal for Stepdads to Share Their Life Story

- Life Gave Me You; I Want to Hear Your Story: A Guided Journal for Stepmothers to Share Their Life Story

- Because I Love You: The Couple's Bucket List That Builds Your Relationship

- Grandfather, I Want to Hear Your Story: A Grandfather's Guided Journal to Share His Life and His Love

- Grandmother, I Want to Hear Your Story: A Grandmother's Guided Journal to Share Her Life and Her Love

- To My Wonderful Aunt, I Want to Hear Your Story: A Guided Journal to Share Her Life and Her Love

- To My Uncle, I Want to Hear Your Story: A Guided Journal to Share His Life and His Love

- Love Notes: I Wrote This Book About You

- Getting to Know You: 201 Fun Questions to Deepen Your Relationship and Hear Each Other's Story

- You, Me, and Us: 229 Fun Relationship Questions to Ask Your Guy or Girl